Exclusive Distributors:
Music Sales Limited
8-9 Frith Street,
London W1V 5TZ, England.
Music Sales Pty Limited
120 Rothschild Avenue,
Rosebery, NSW 2018, Australia.

Order No. HLE90000308
ISBN 0-7119-6457-2

Cover design by Pearce Marchbank and Ben May, Studio Twenty, London.
Printed in the USA.

Great Songs of the Fifties

Your Guarantee of Quality
As publishers, we strive to produce every book to the highest commercial standards.
This book has been carefully designed to minimise awkward page turns and
to make playing from it a real pleasure.
Throughout, the printing and binding have been planned to ensure a sturdy,
attractive publication which should give years of enjoyment.
If your copy fails to meet our high standards,
please inform us and we will gladly replace it.

Music Sales' complete catalogue describes thousands of titles
and is available in full colour sections by subject,
direct from Music Sales Limited.
Please state your areas of interest and
send a cheque/postal order for £1.50 for postage to:
Music Sales Limited, Newmarket Road,
Bury St. Edmunds, Suffolk IP33 3YB.

Visit the Internet Music Shop at
http://www.musicsales.co.uk

FOR ORGANS, PIANOS & ELECTRONIC KEYBOARDS
EZPLAY TODAY
9

HLE
Hal Leonard Europe
Distributed by Music Sales

All I Have to Do Is Dream

Registration 2
Rhythm: Slow Rock or Fox Trot

By Boudleaux Bryant

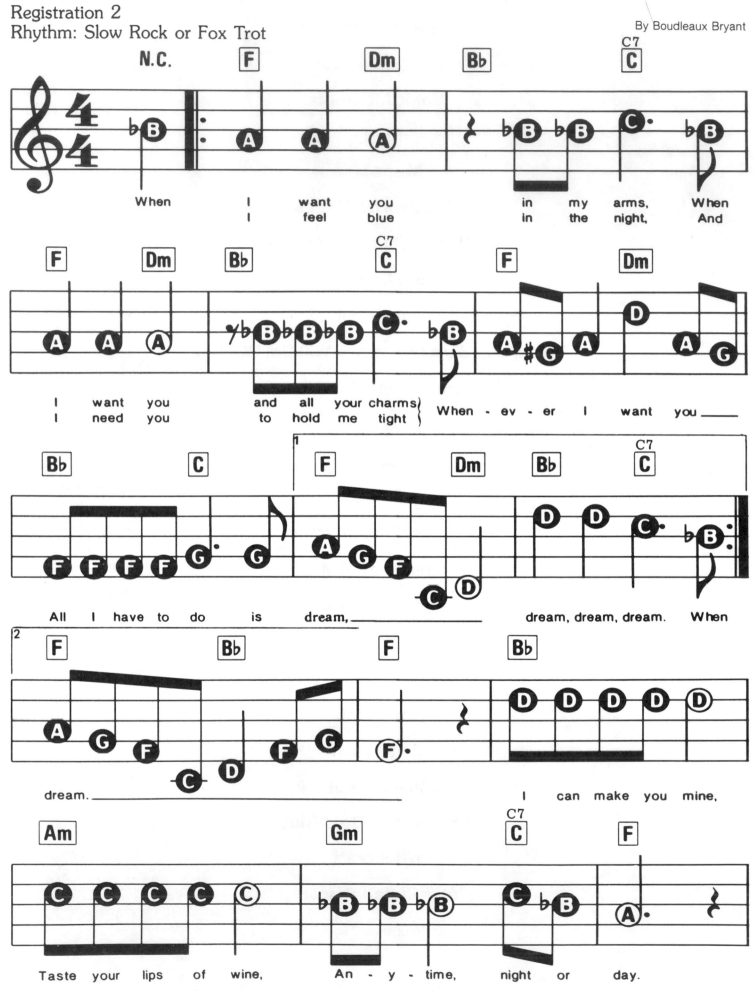

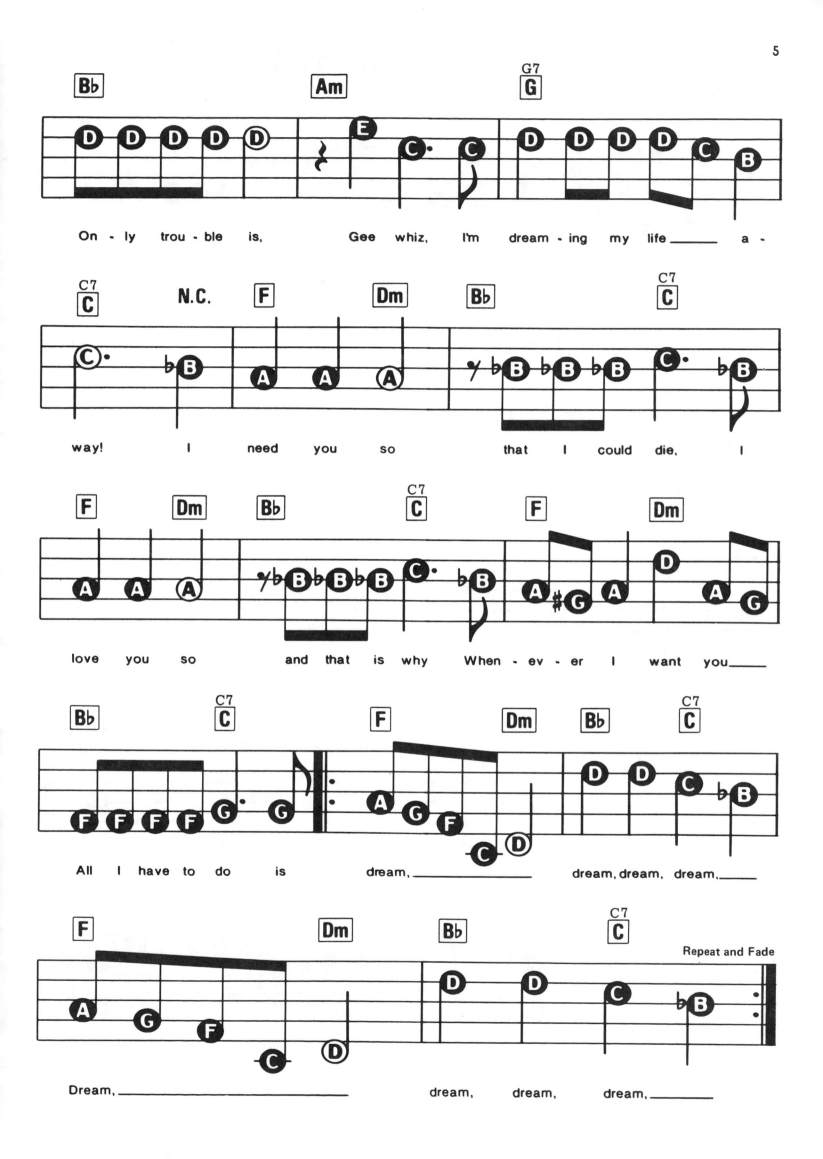

All Shook Up

Registration 5
Rhythm: Rock

Words and Music by
Otis Blackwell and Elvis Presley

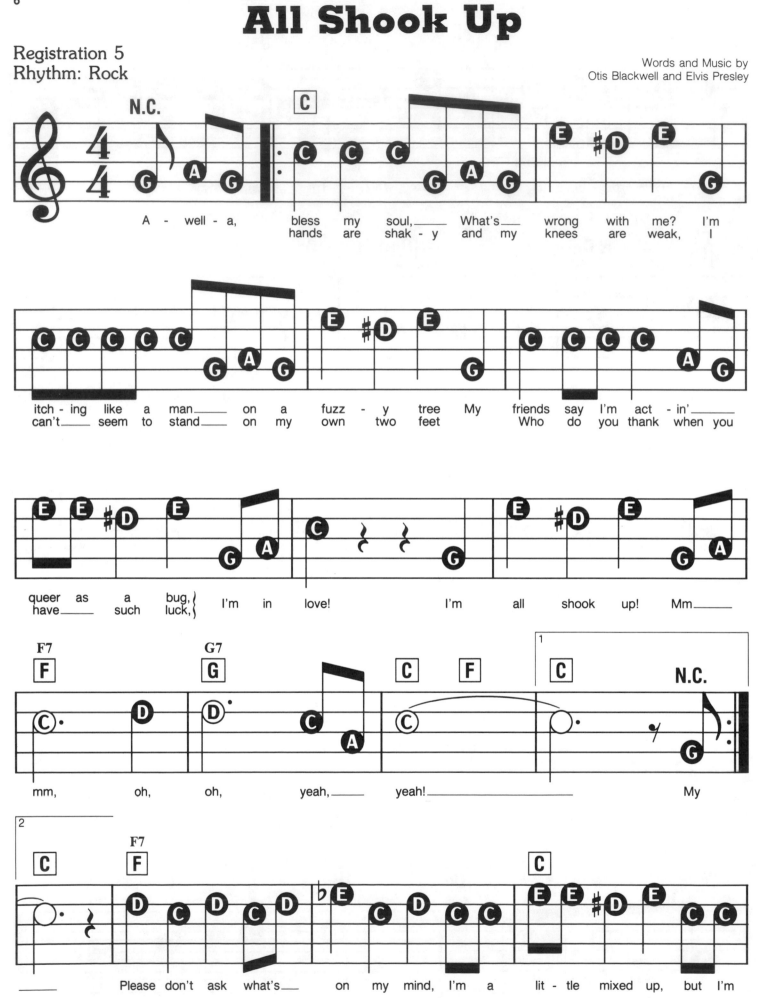

7

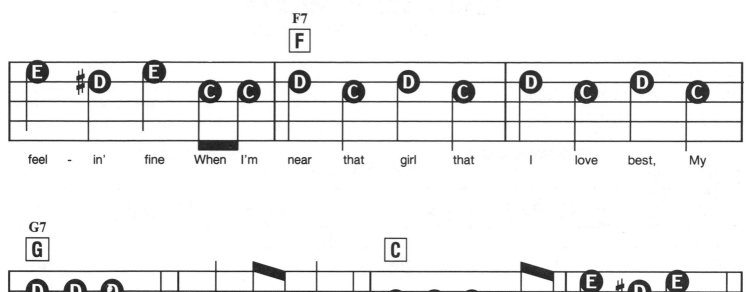

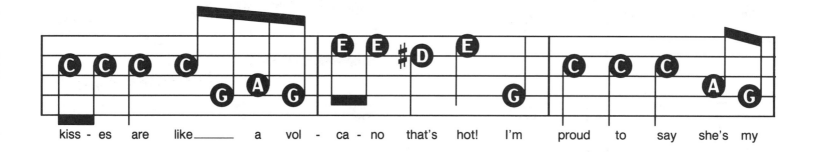

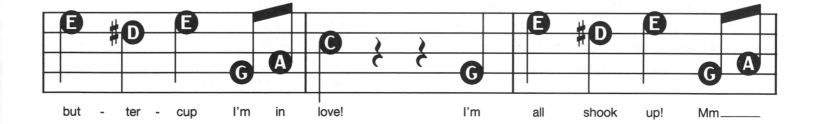

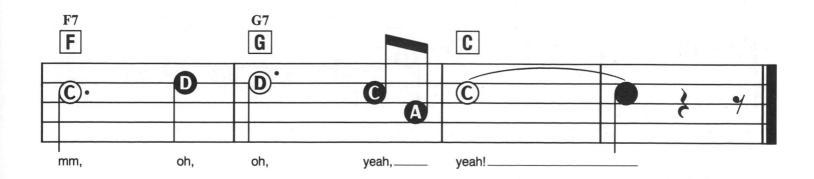

All the Way
from THE JOKER IS WILD

Registration 3
Rhythm: Fox Trot or Ballad

Words by Sammy Cahn
Music by James Van Heusen

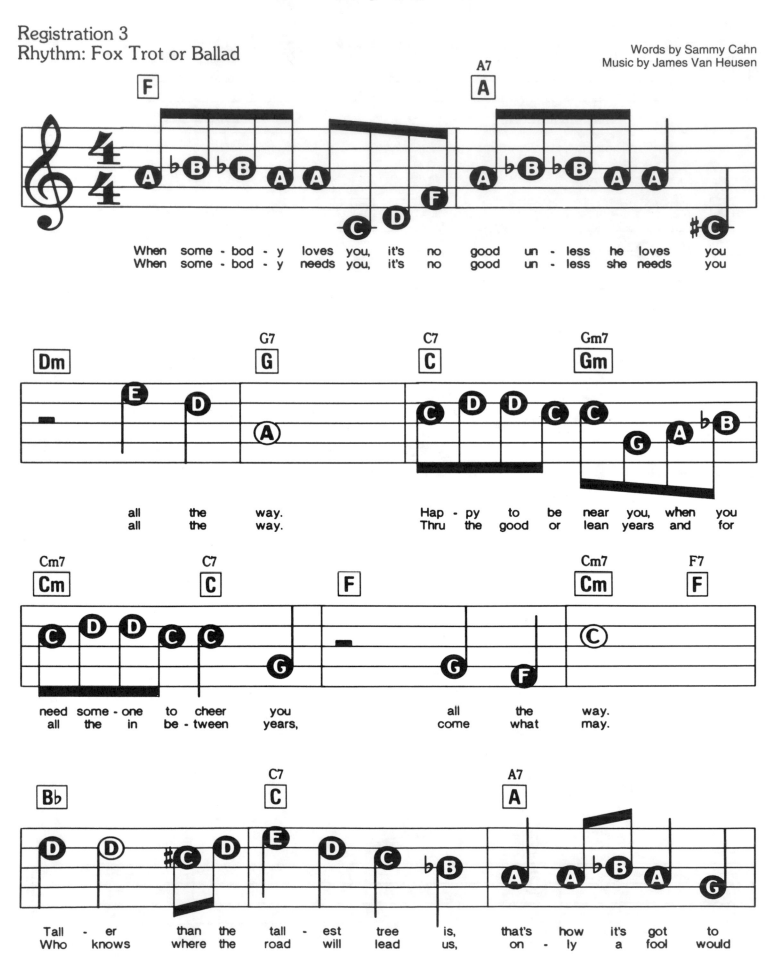

When some - bod - y loves you, it's no good un - less he loves you
When some - bod - y needs you, it's no good un - less she needs you

all the way.
all the way.

Hap - py to be near you, when you
Thru the good or lean years and for

need some - one to cheer you all the way.
all the in be - tween years, come what may.

Tall - er than the tall - est tree is, that's how it's got to
Who knows where the road will lead us, on - ly a fool would

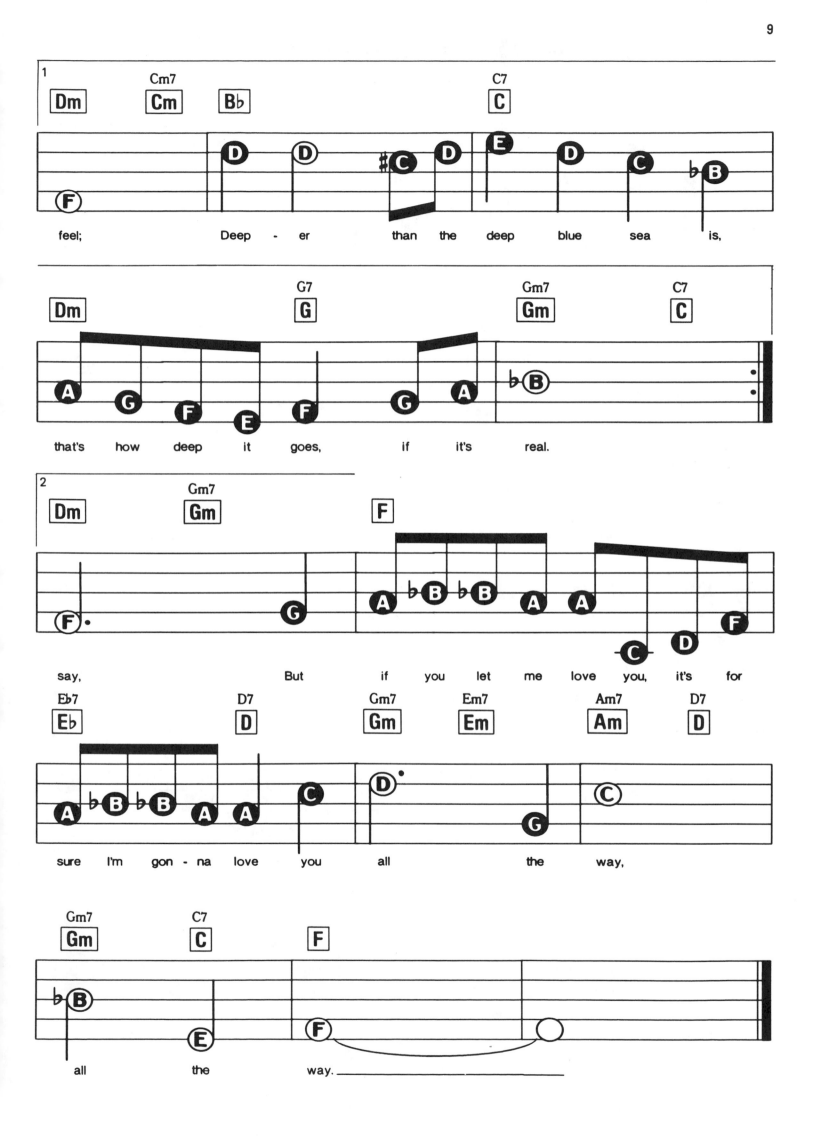

Alright, Okay, You Win

Registration 7
Rhythm: Swing

Words and Music by Sid Wyche
and Mayme Watts

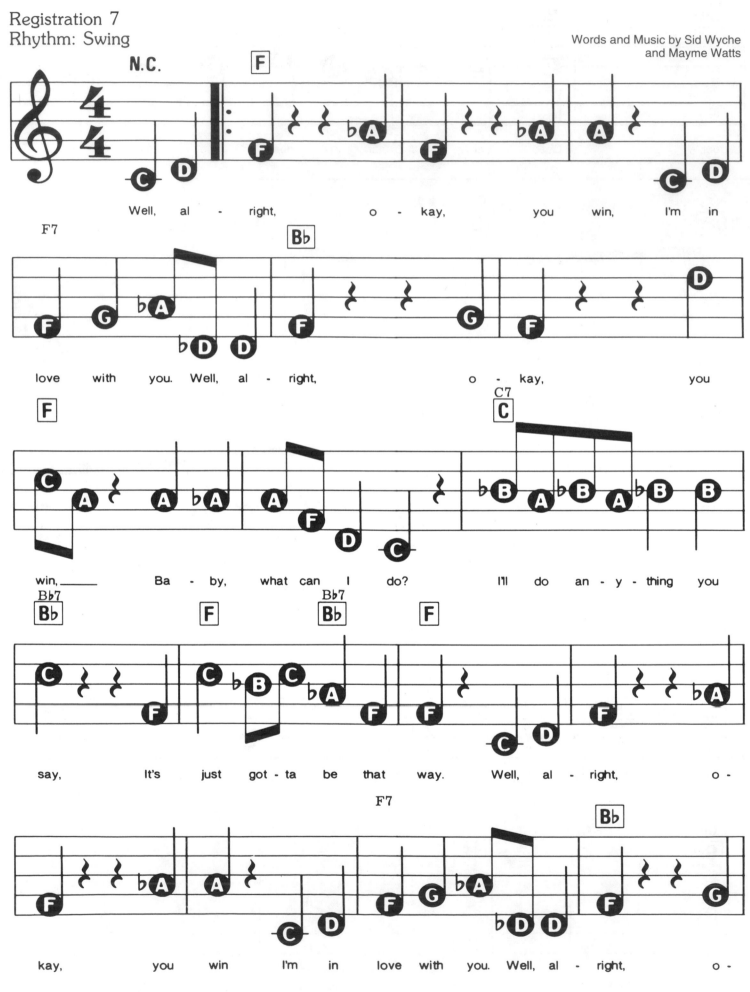

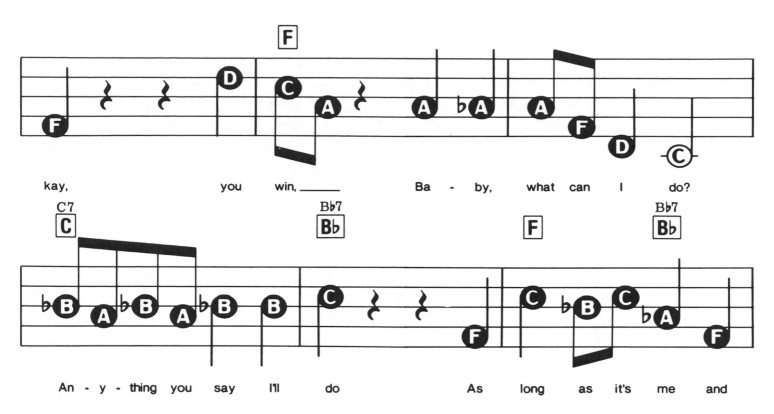

kay, you win, _____ Ba - by, what can I do?

An - y - thing you say I'll do As long as it's me and

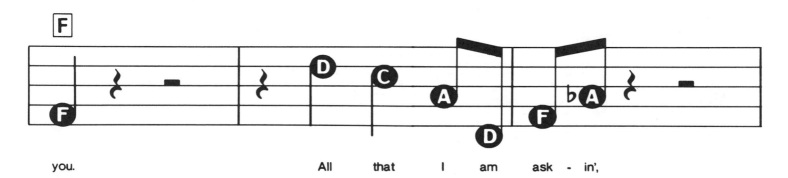

you. All that I am ask - in',

All I want from you, Just love me like

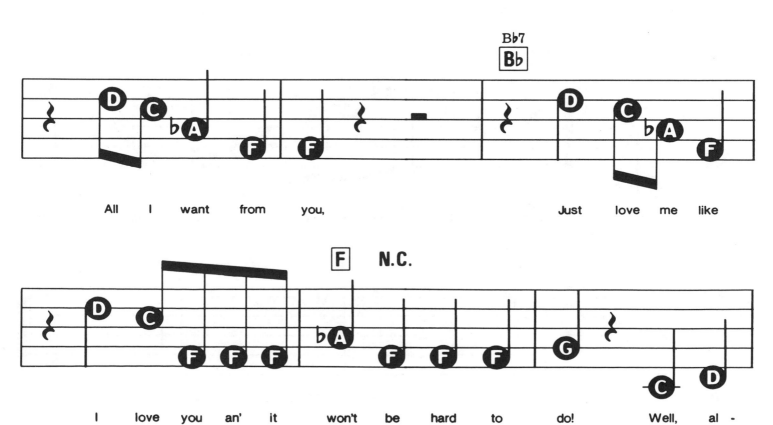

I love you an' it won't be hard to do! Well, al -

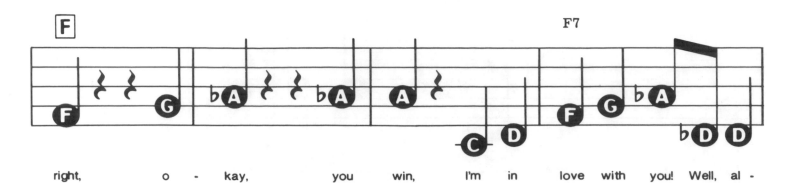

right, o - kay, you win, I'm in love with you! Well, al -

right, o - kay, you win, _____ {Ba - by, what can I do?
Ba - by, one ____ thing more

I'll do an - y - thing you say. It's just got to be that
If you're gon - na be my

way. Well, al - man. Sweet ba - by take me by the hand, Well, al -

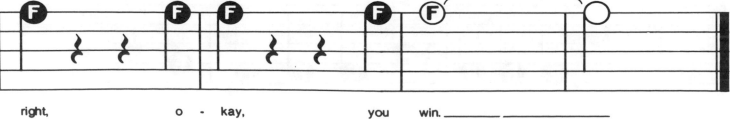

right, o - kay, you win. _____ _____

Angel Eyes

Registration 9
Rhythm: Fox Trot or Swing

Words by Earl Brent
Music by Matt Dennis

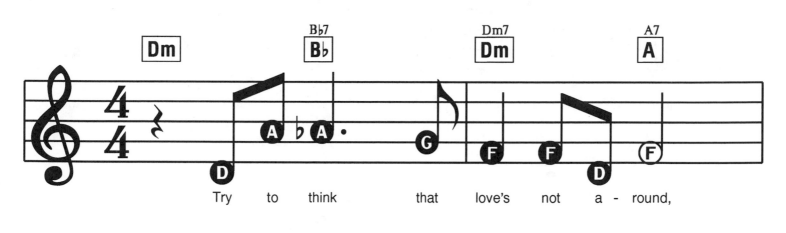

Try to think that love's not a - round,

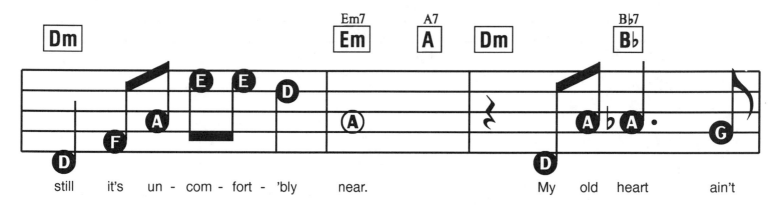

still it's un - com - fort - 'bly near. My old heart ain't

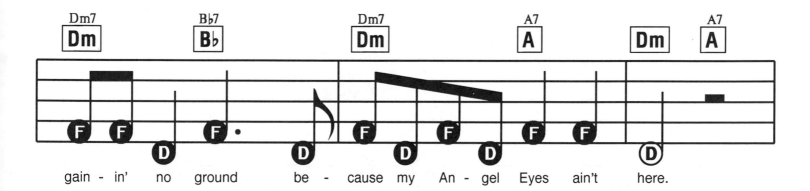

gain - in' no ground be - cause my An - gel Eyes ain't here.

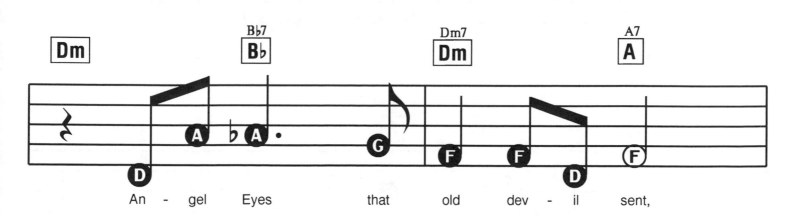

An - gel Eyes that old dev - il sent,

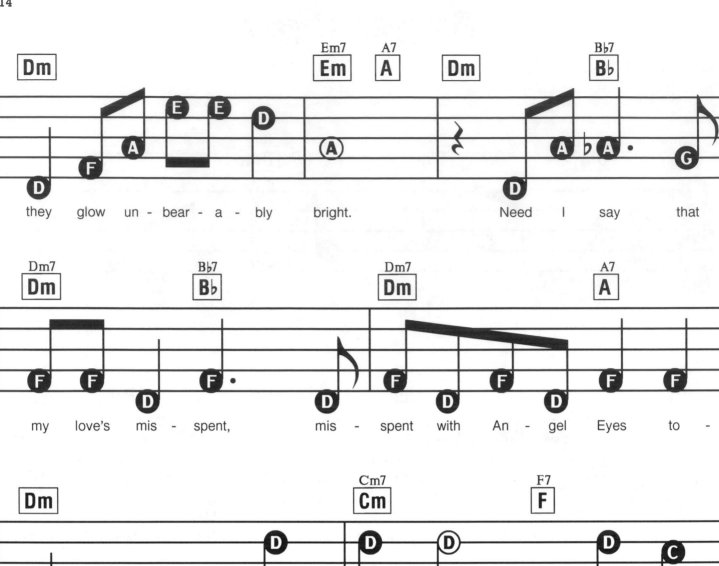

they glow un-bear-a-bly bright.   Need I say that

my love's mis-spent,   mis-spent with An-gel Eyes to-

night.   So   drink   up   all   you

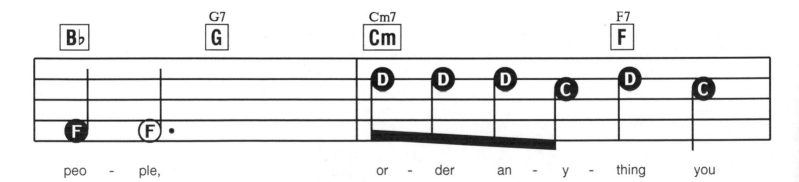

peo - ple,   or - der an - y - thing you

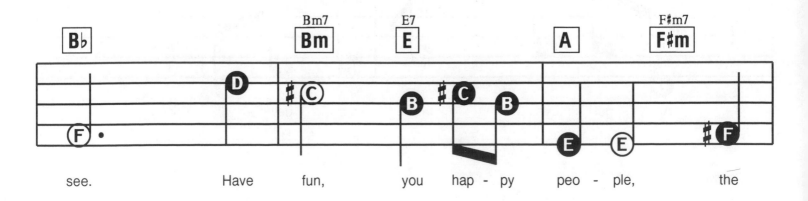

see.   Have   fun,   you hap-py peo - ple,   the

Arrivederci Roma
(Goodbye to Rome)
from the Motion Picture SEVEN HILLS OF ROME

Registration 3
Rhythm: Latin

Words by Carl Sigman
Music by R. Rascel

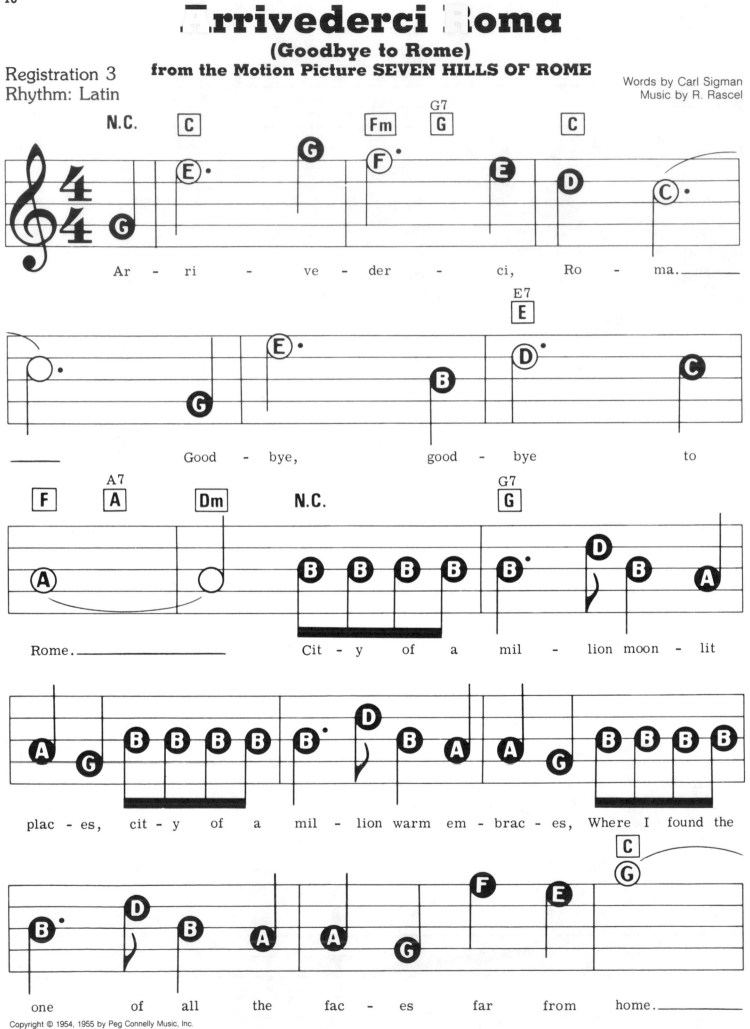

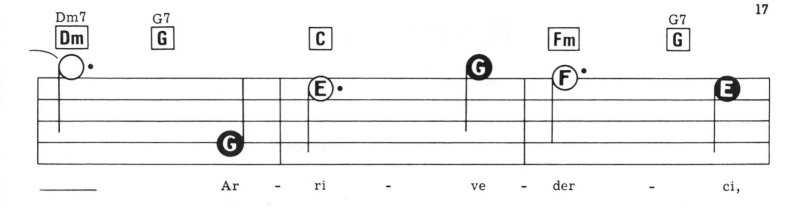

Ar - ri - ve - der - ci,

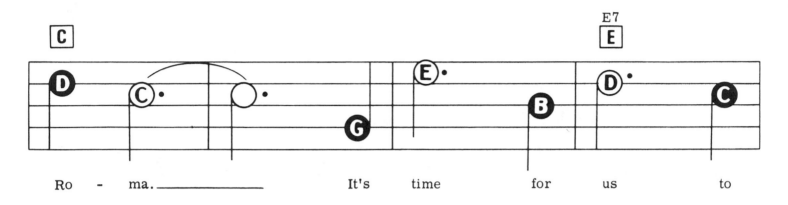

Ro - ma. _____ It's time for us to

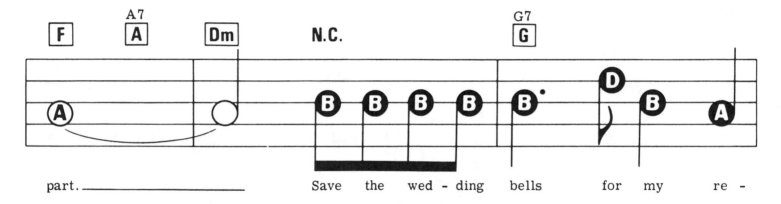

part. _____ Save the wed - ding bells for my re -

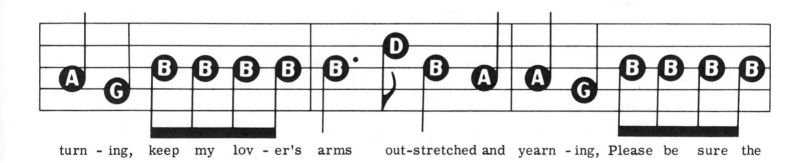

turn - ing, keep my lov - er's arms out-stretched and yearn - ing, Please be sure the

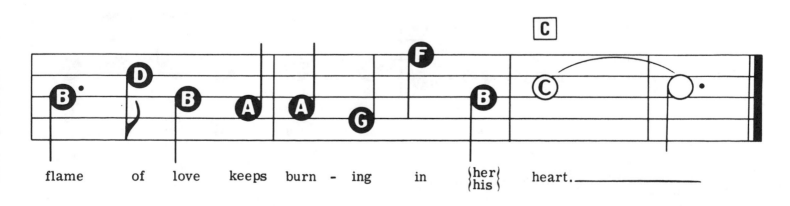

flame of love keeps burn - ing in {her}{his} heart. _____

At the Hop

Registration 5
Rhythm: Rock

Words and Music by Arthur Singer,
John Medora and David White

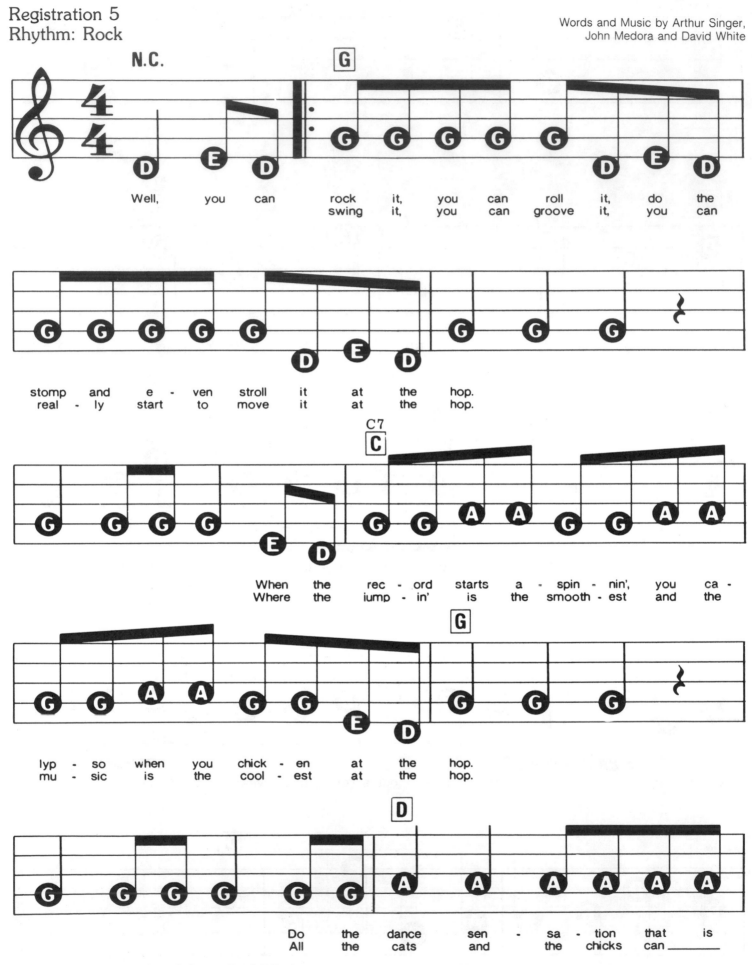

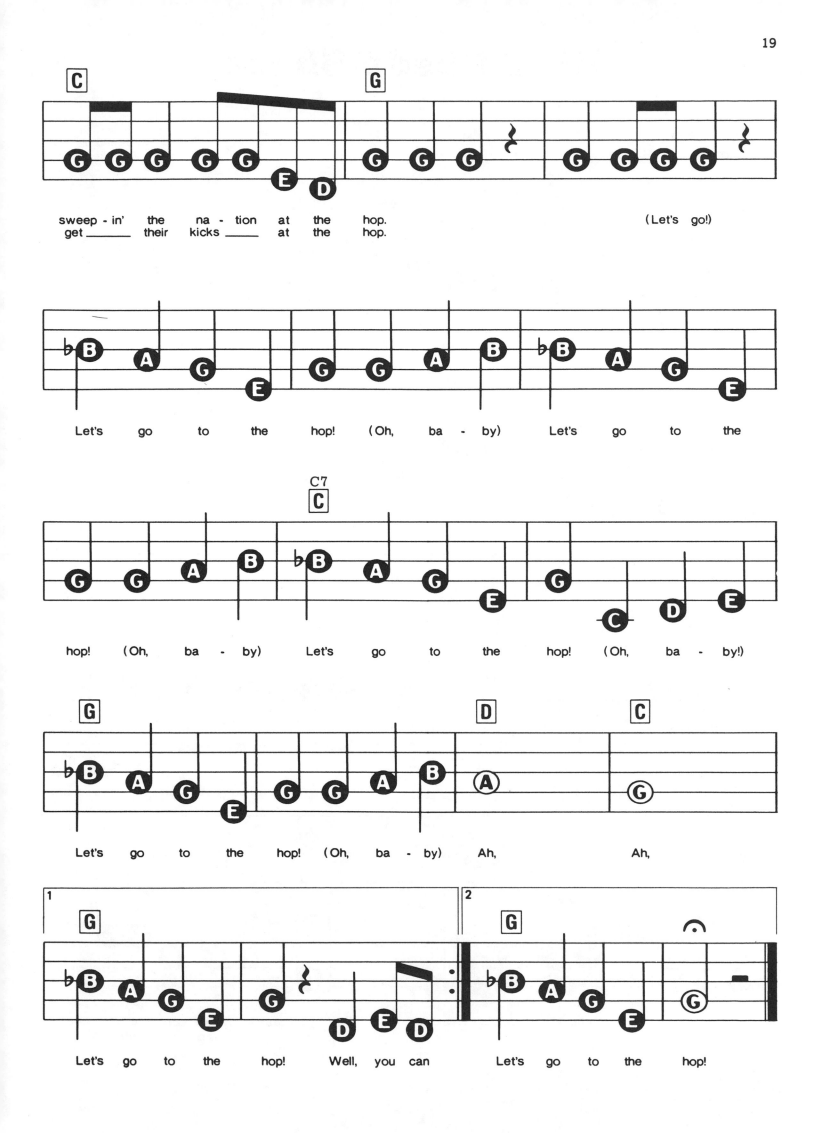

Blue Suede Shoes

Registration 5
Rhythm: Rock

Words and Music by
Carl Lee Perkins

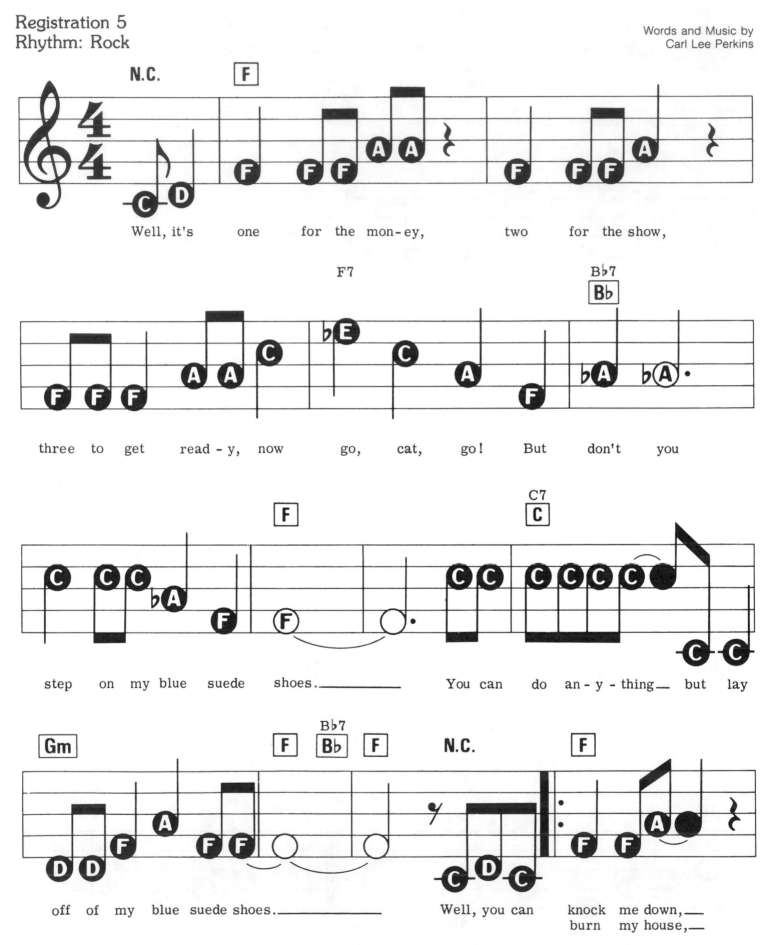

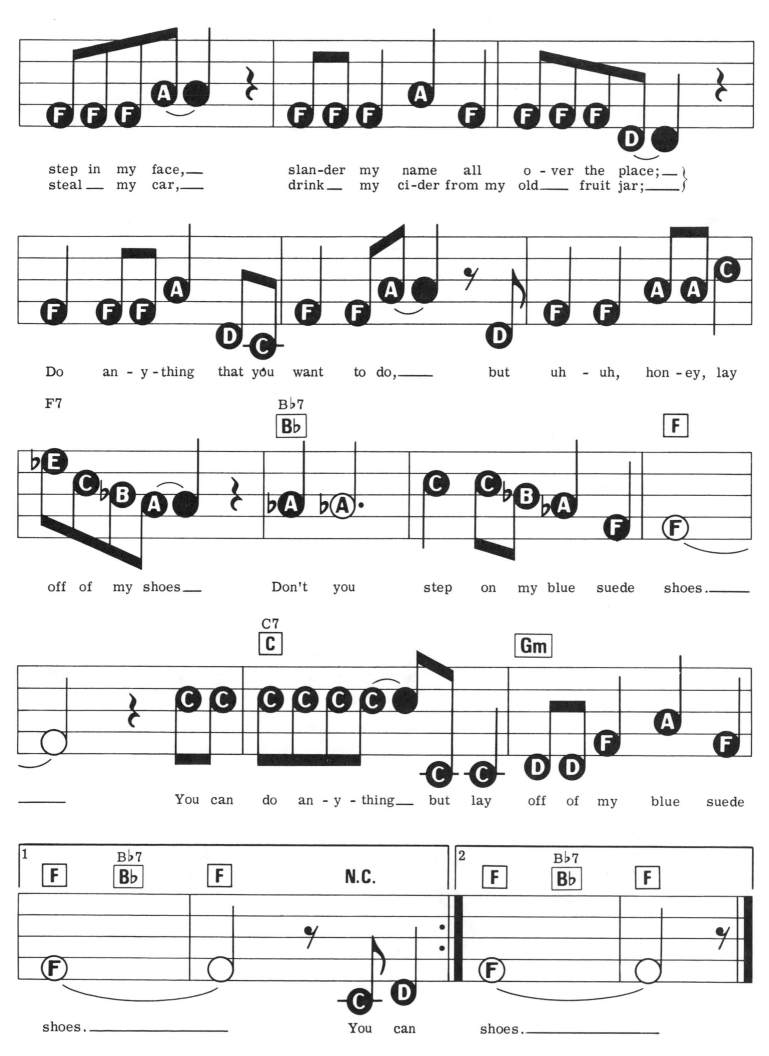

step in my face,— slan-der my name all o-ver the place;—
steal— my car,— drink— my ci-der from my old— fruit jar;—

Do an-y-thing that you want to do,— but uh-uh, hon-ey, lay

F7   Bb7 [Bb]   [F]

off of my shoes— Don't you step on my blue suede shoes.—

C7 [C]   [Gm]

—— You can do an-y-thing— but lay off of my blue suede

1 [F] Bb7 [Bb] [F] N.C.   2 [F] Bb7 [Bb] [F]

shoes.————— You can shoes.———

Blue Velvet

Registration 1
Rhythm: Fox Trot or Swing

Words and Music by
Bernie Wayne and Lee Morris

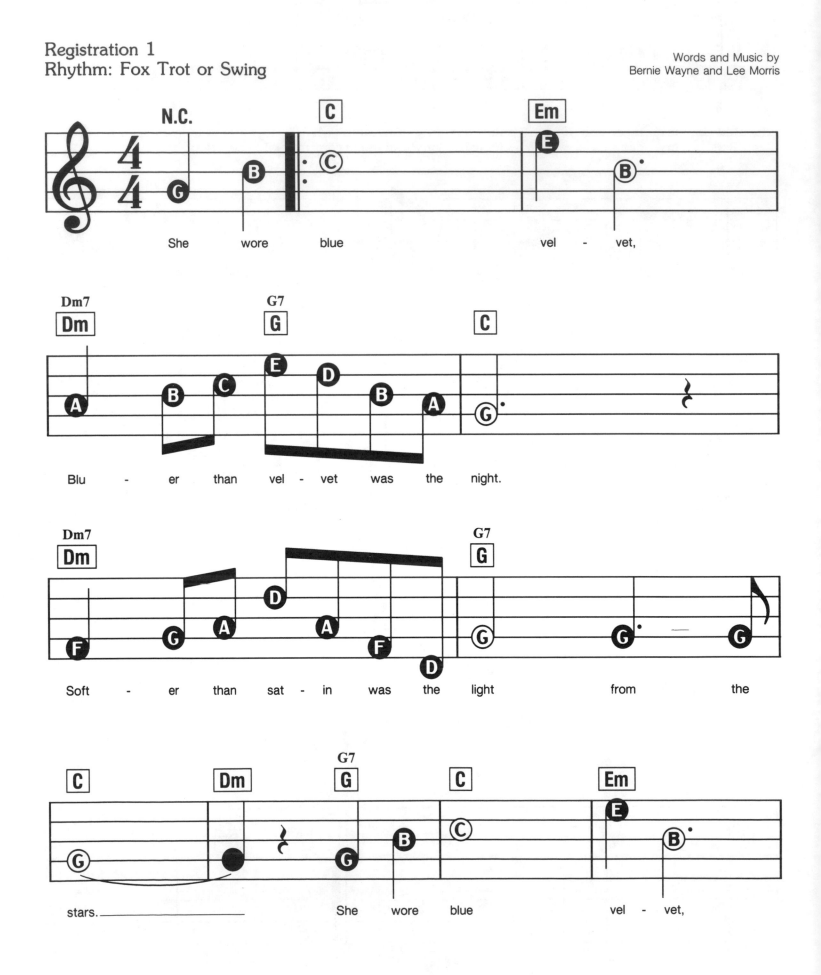

23

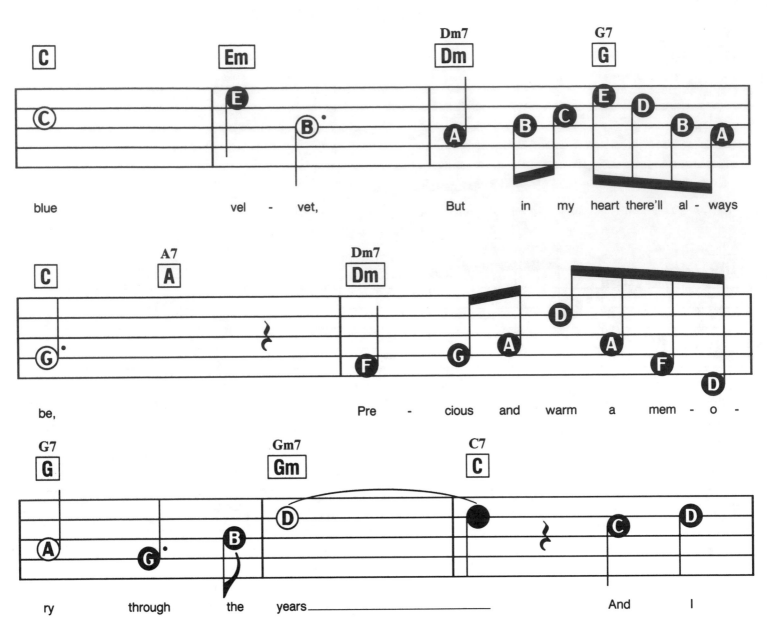

blue   vel - vet,   But   in   my   heart there'll al - ways

be,   Pre - cious and warm a mem - o -

ry   through   the   years   And   I

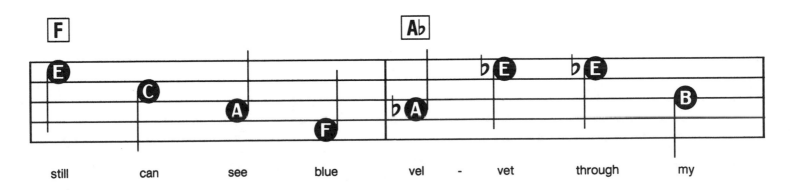

still   can   see   blue   vel - vet   through   my

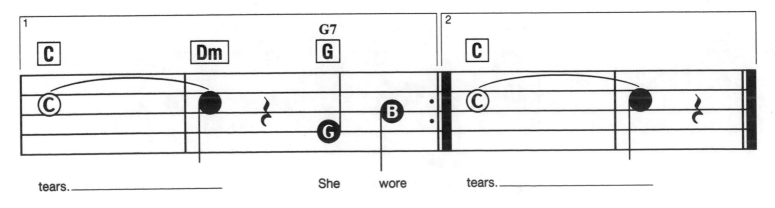

tears.   She wore   tears.

Bye Bye Love

Registration 4
Rhythm: Fox Trot or Swing

Words and Music by
Felice Bryant and Boudleaux Bryant

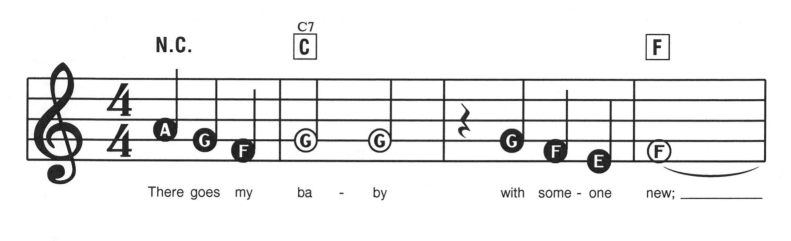

There goes my ba - by with some - one new; _____

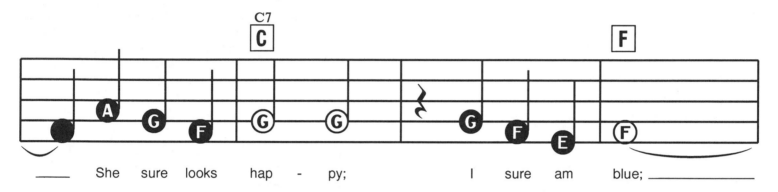

_____ She sure looks hap - py; I sure am blue; _____

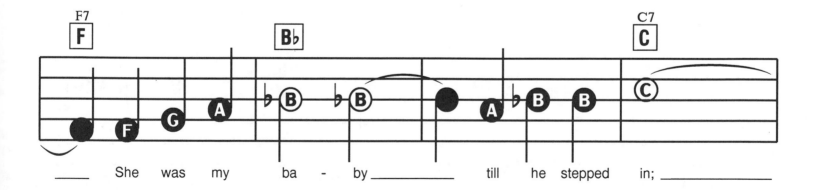

_____ She was my ba - by _____ till he stepped in; _____

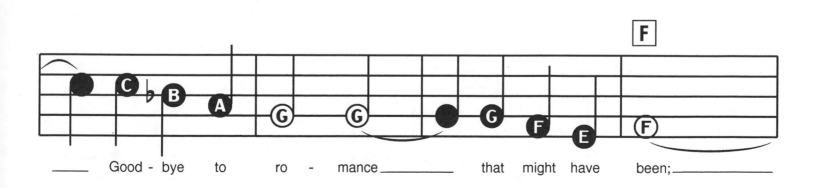

_____ Good - bye to ro - mance _____ that might have been; _____

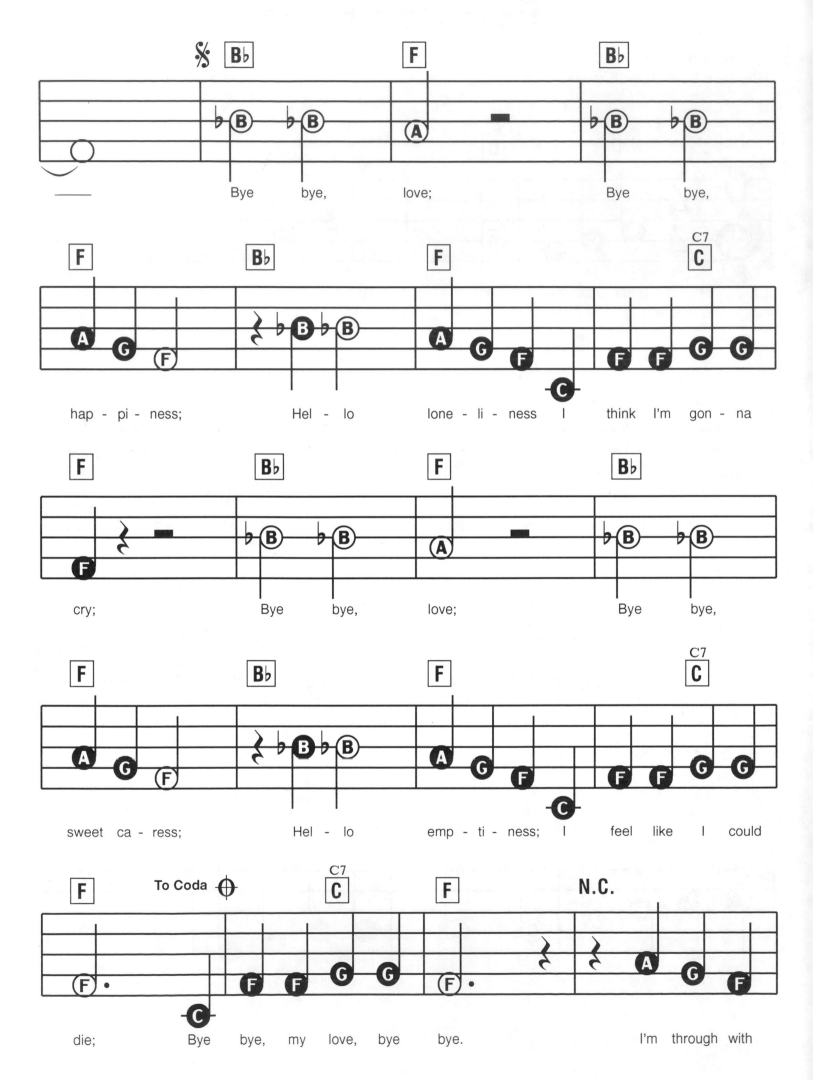

26

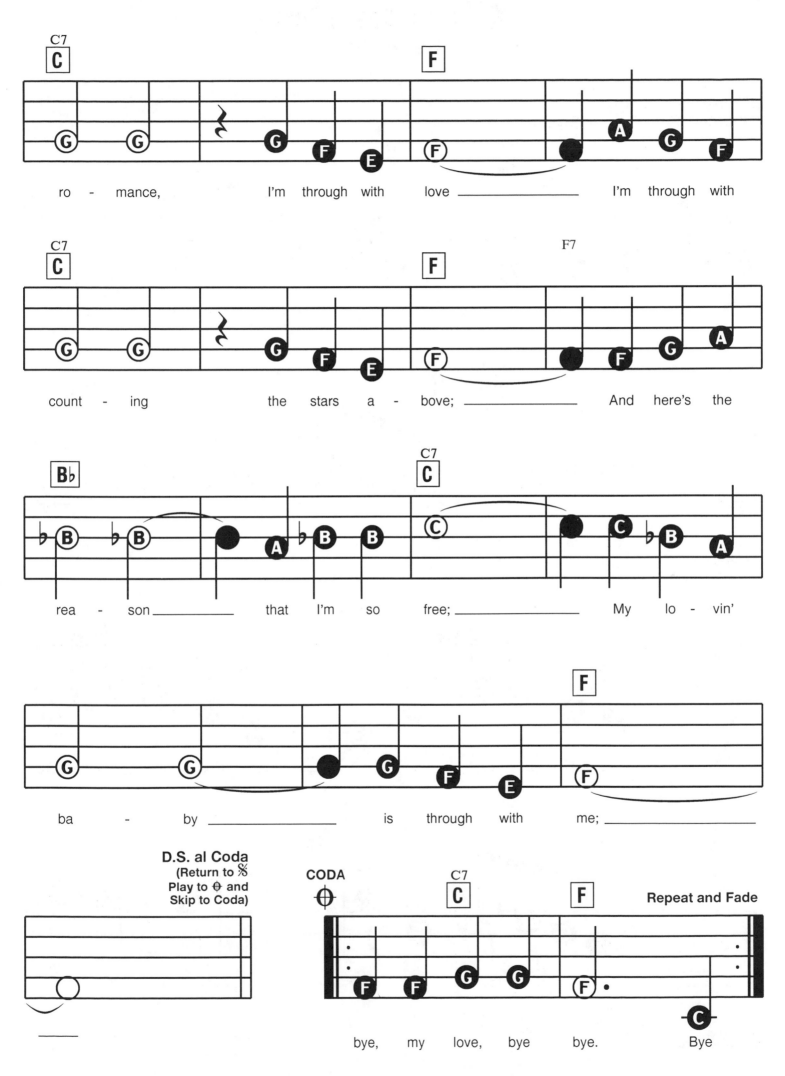

C'est Si Bon
(It's So Good)

Registration 2
Rhythm: Fox Trot or Swing

English Words by Jerry Seelen
French Words by Andre Hornez
Music by Henri Betti

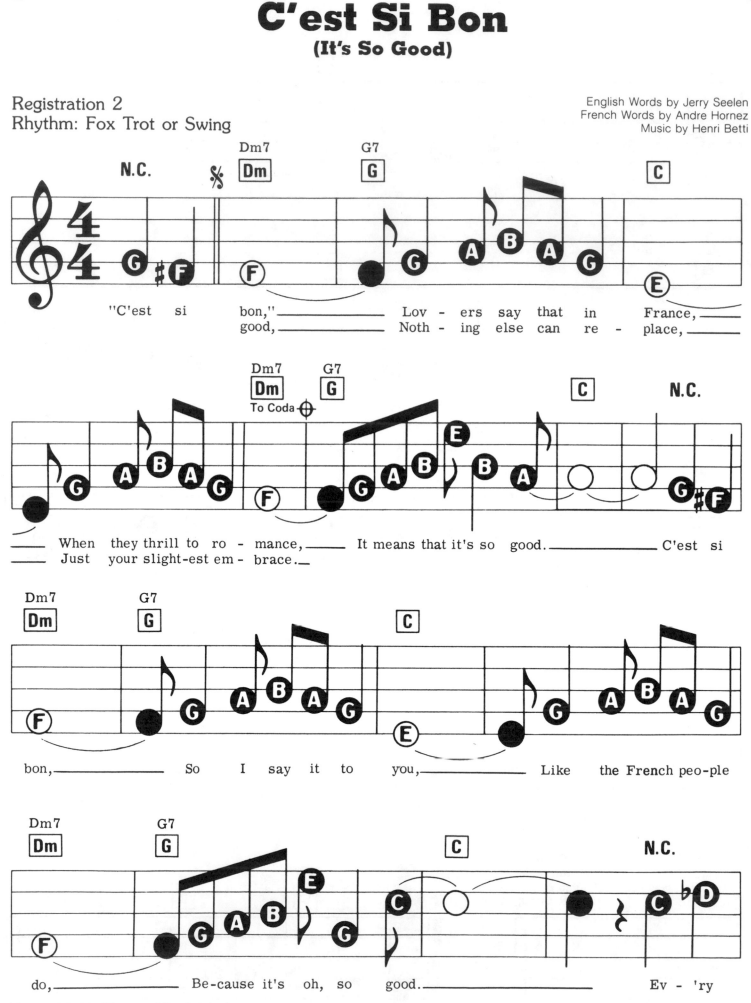

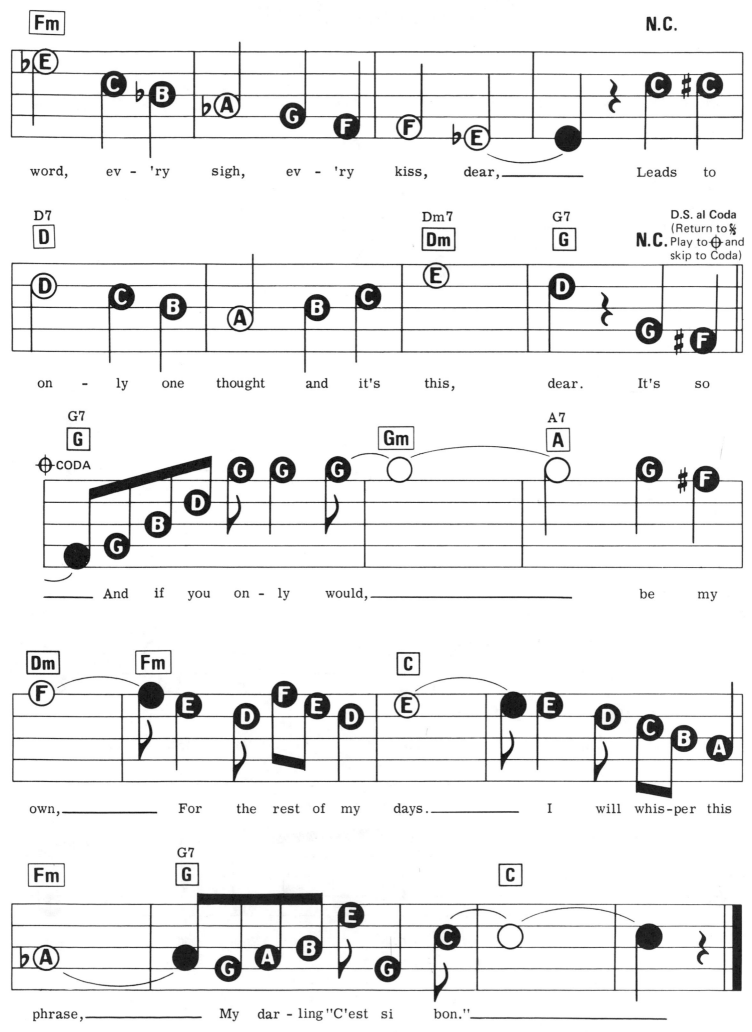

Chantilly Lace

Registration 8
Rhythm: Rock'n'Roll or Rock

Words and Music by
J.P. Richardson

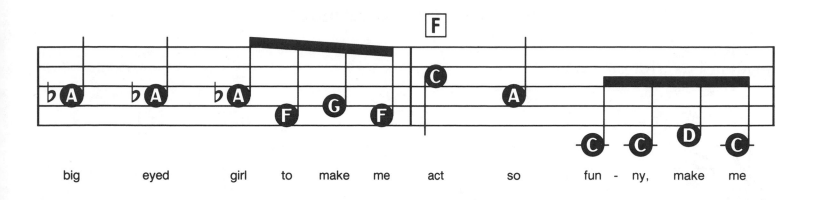

big   eyed   girl   to   make   me   act   so   fun - ny,   make   me

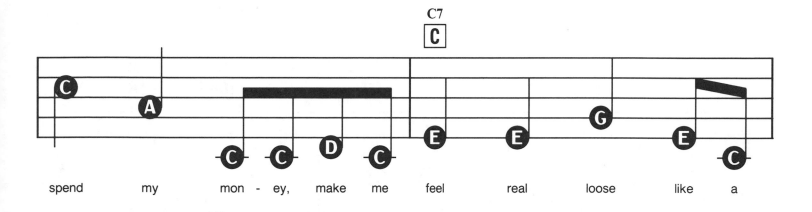

spend   my   mon - ey,   make   me   feel   real   loose   like   a

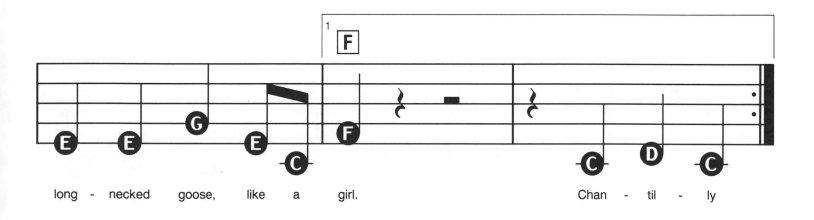

long - necked   goose,   like   a   girl.   Chan - til - ly

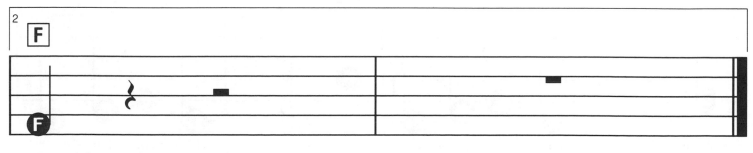

girl. *Spoken: Oh,   Baby,   that's - a   what   I   like.*

Climb Ev'ry Mountain
from THE SOUND OF MUSIC

Registration 5
Rhythm: Fox Trot or Swing

Words by Oscar Hammerstein II
Music by Richard Rodgers

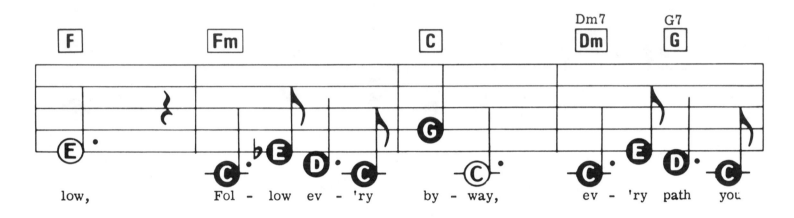

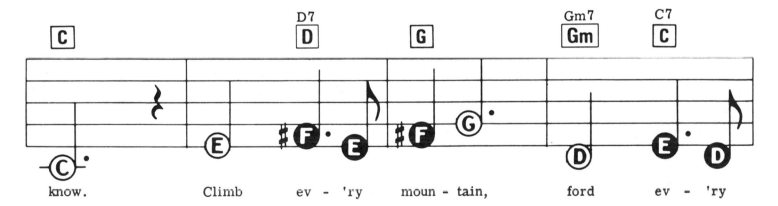

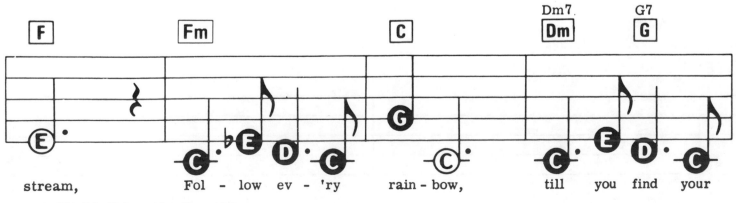

33

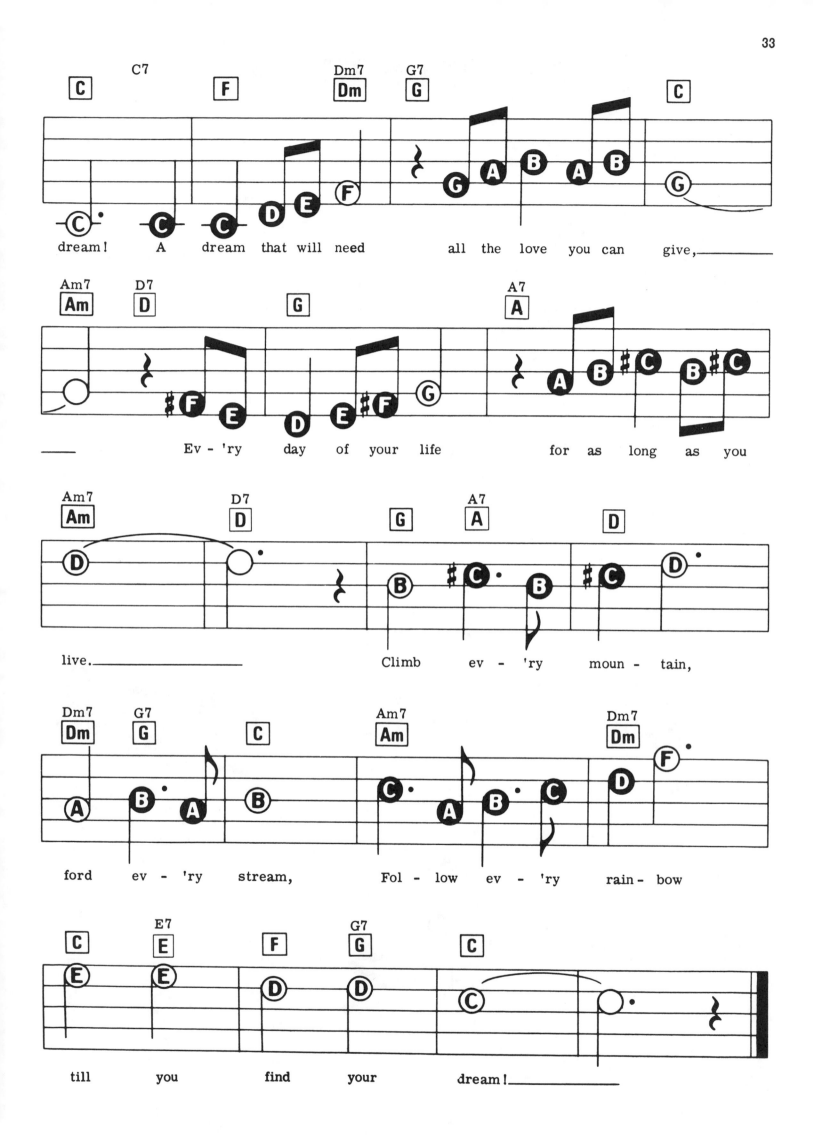

Cry Me a River

Registration 2
Rhythm: Fox Trot

Words and Music by
Arthur Hamilton

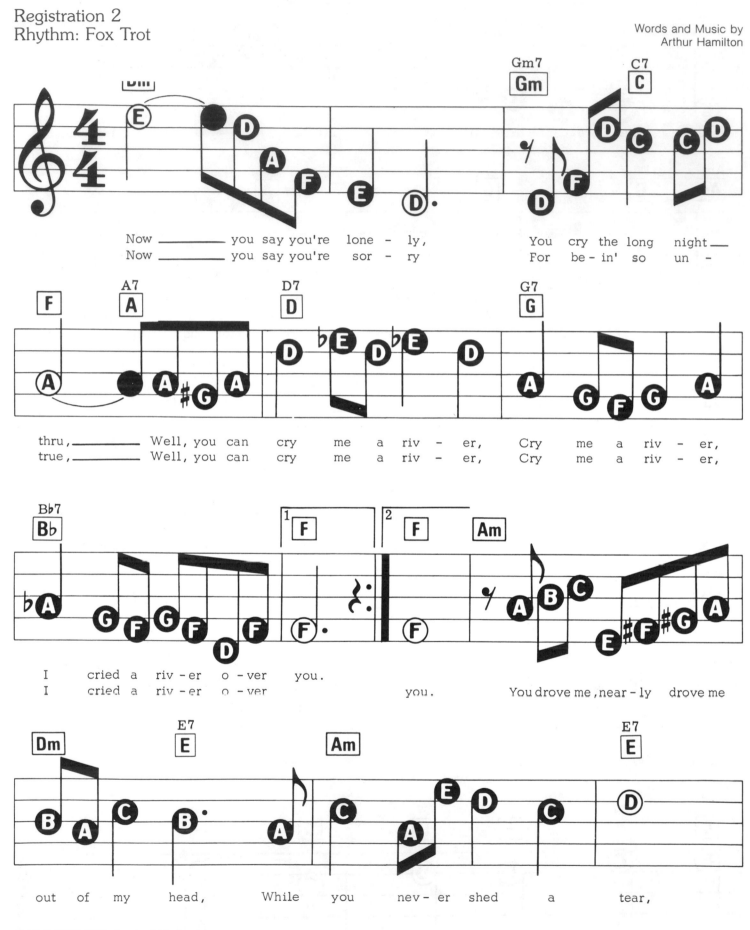

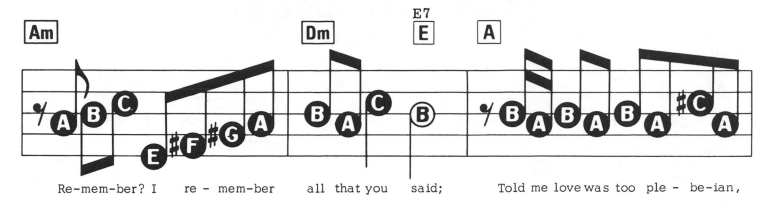

Re-mem-ber? I re - mem-ber all that you said; Told me love was too ple - be-ian,

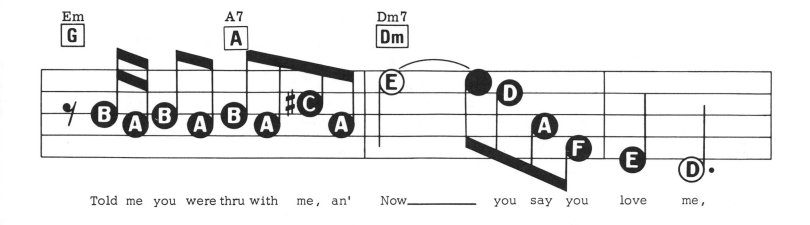

Told me you were thru with me, an' Now_____ you say you love me,

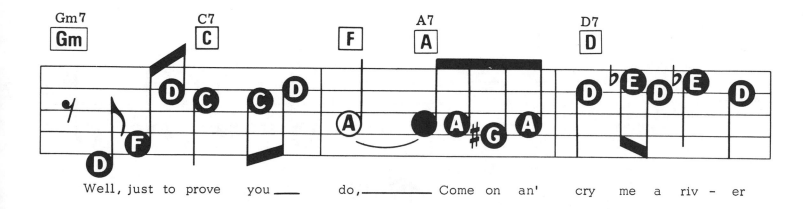

Well, just to prove you ___ do,_____ Come on an' cry me a riv - er

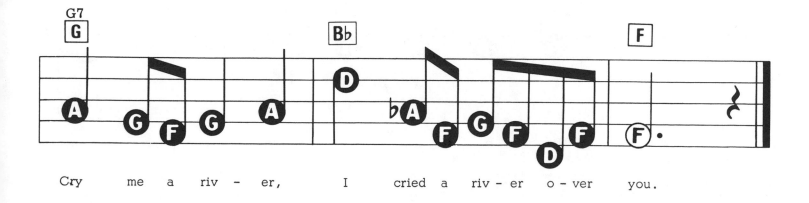

Cry me a riv - er, I cried a riv - er o - ver you.

Don't Be Cruel
(To a Heart That's True)

Registration 4
Rhythm: Rock

Words and Music by
Otis Blackwell and Elvis Presley

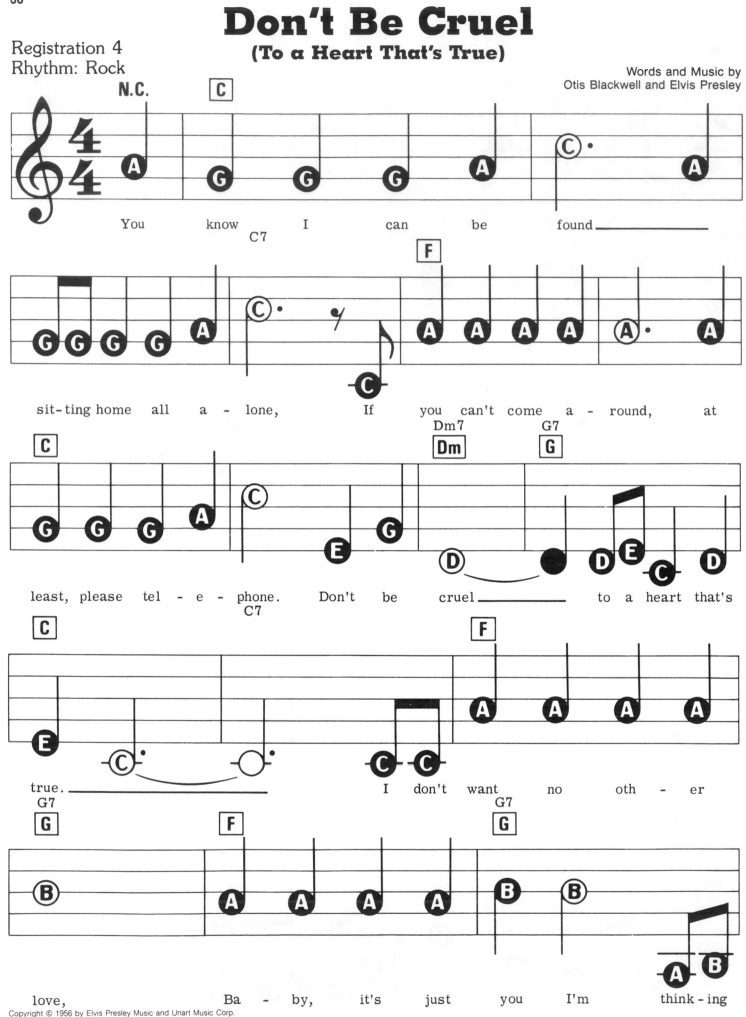

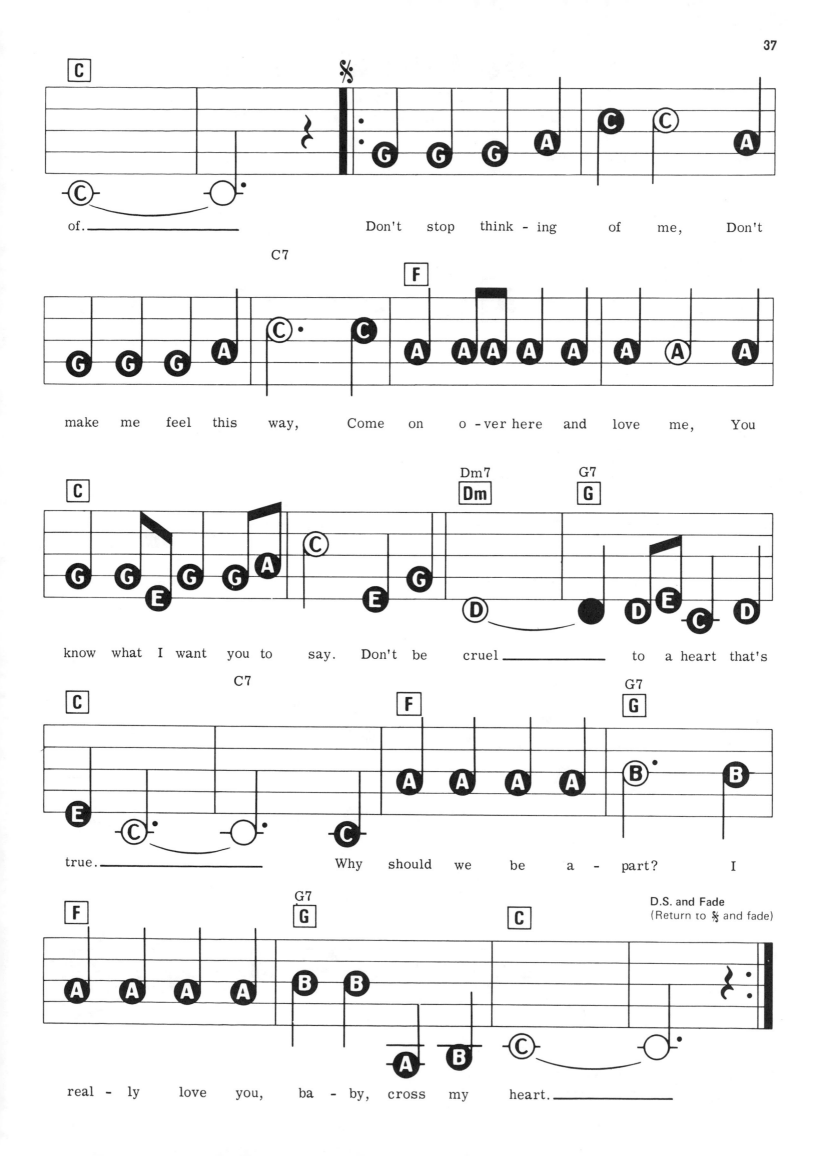

Fly Me to the Moon
(In Other Words)
featured in the Motion Picture ONCE AROUND

Registration 2
Rhythm: Waltz or Jazz Waltz

Words and Music by
Bart Howard

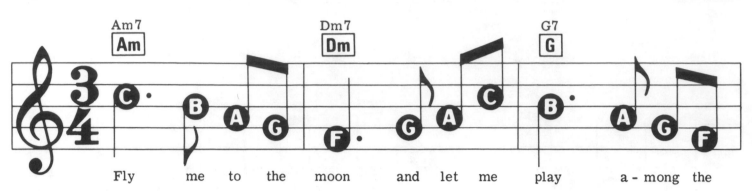

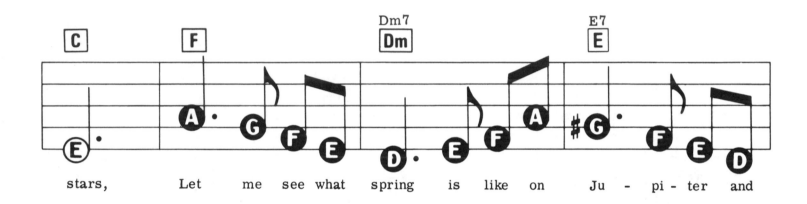

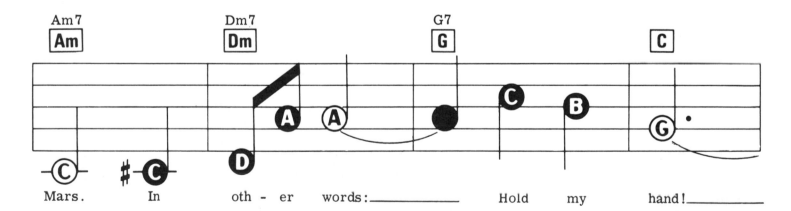

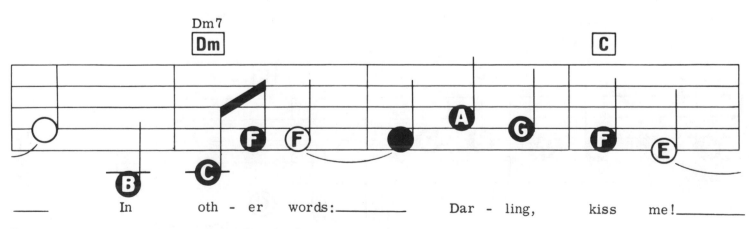

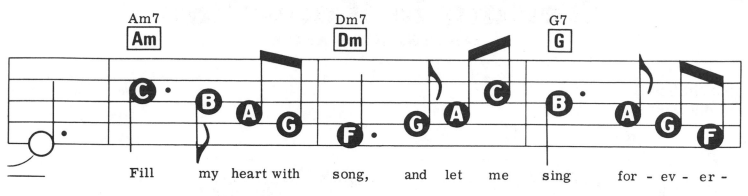

Fill my heart with song, and let me sing for - ev - er -

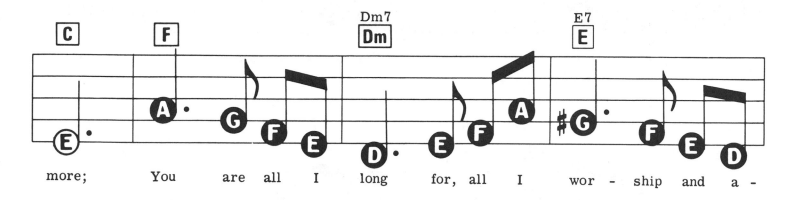

more; You are all I long for, all I wor - ship and a -

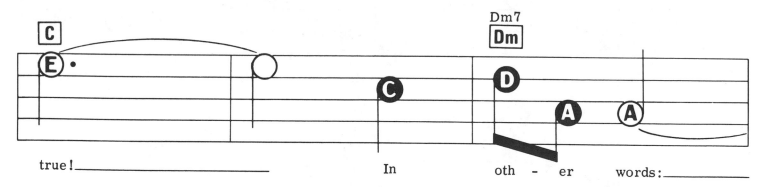

dore. In oth - er words:_____ Please be

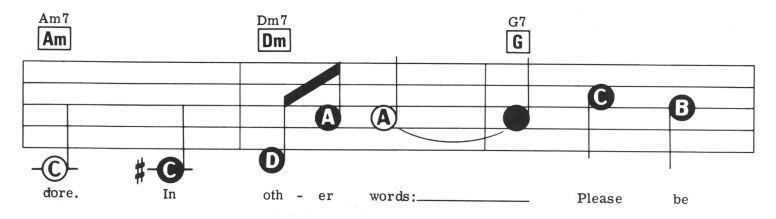

true!_____ In oth - er words:_____

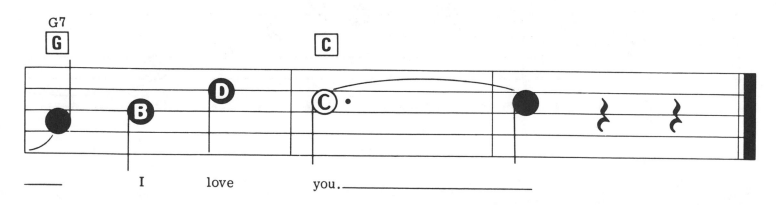

I love you._____

Getting to Know You
from THE KING AND I

Lyrics by Oscar Hammerstein II
Music by Richard Rodgers

Registration 8
Rhythm: Fox Trot or Swing

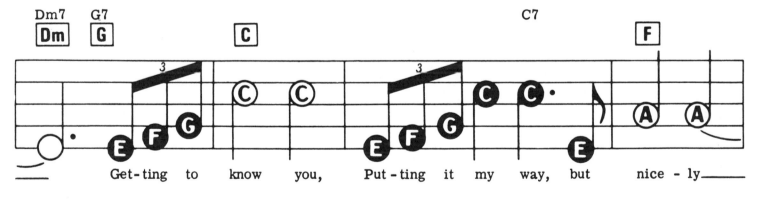

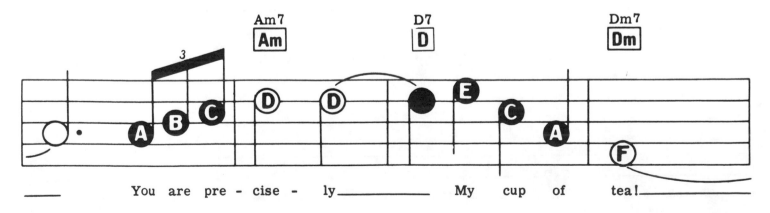

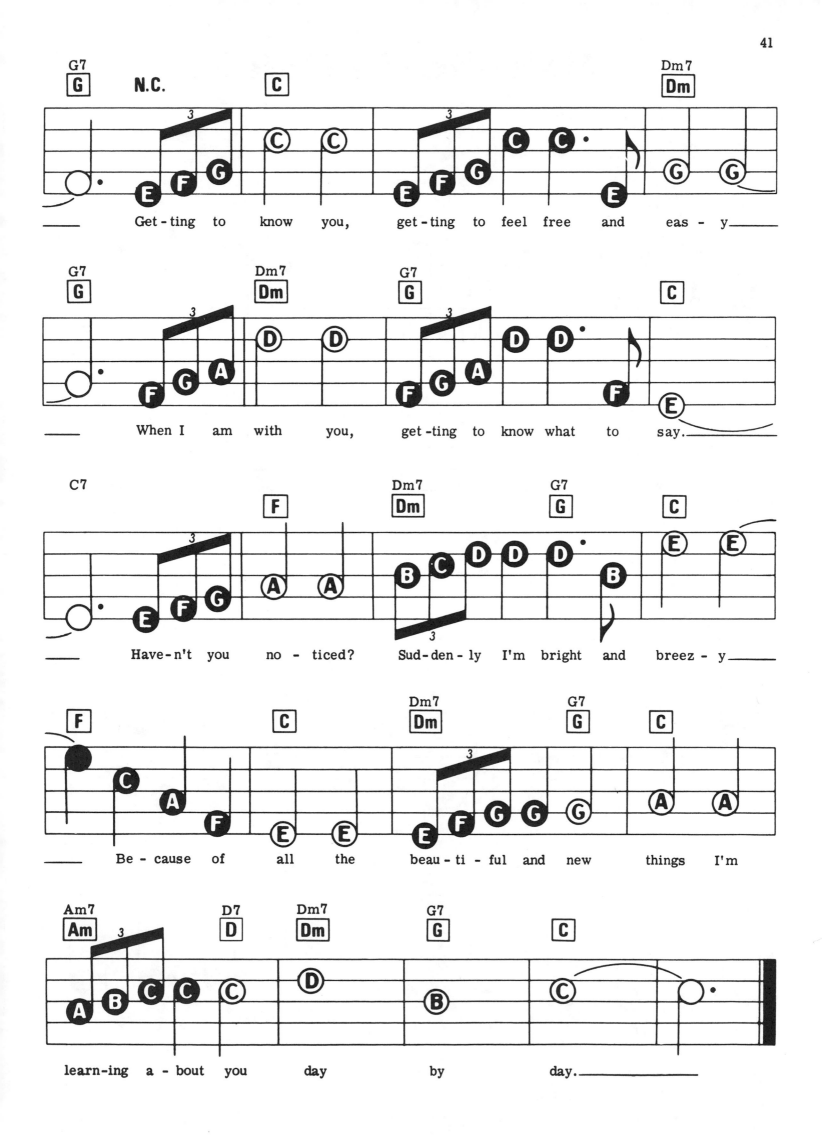

Heartbreak Hotel

Registration 3
Rhythm: Rock or 8 Beat

By Mae Boren Axton, Tommy Durden
and Elvis Presley

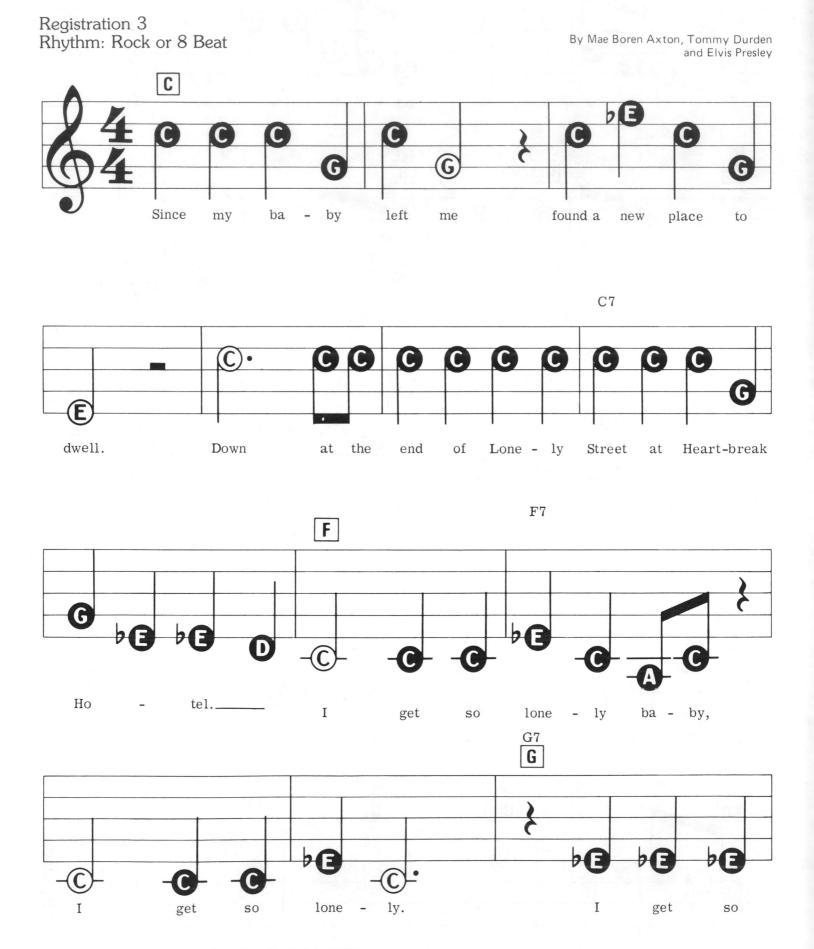

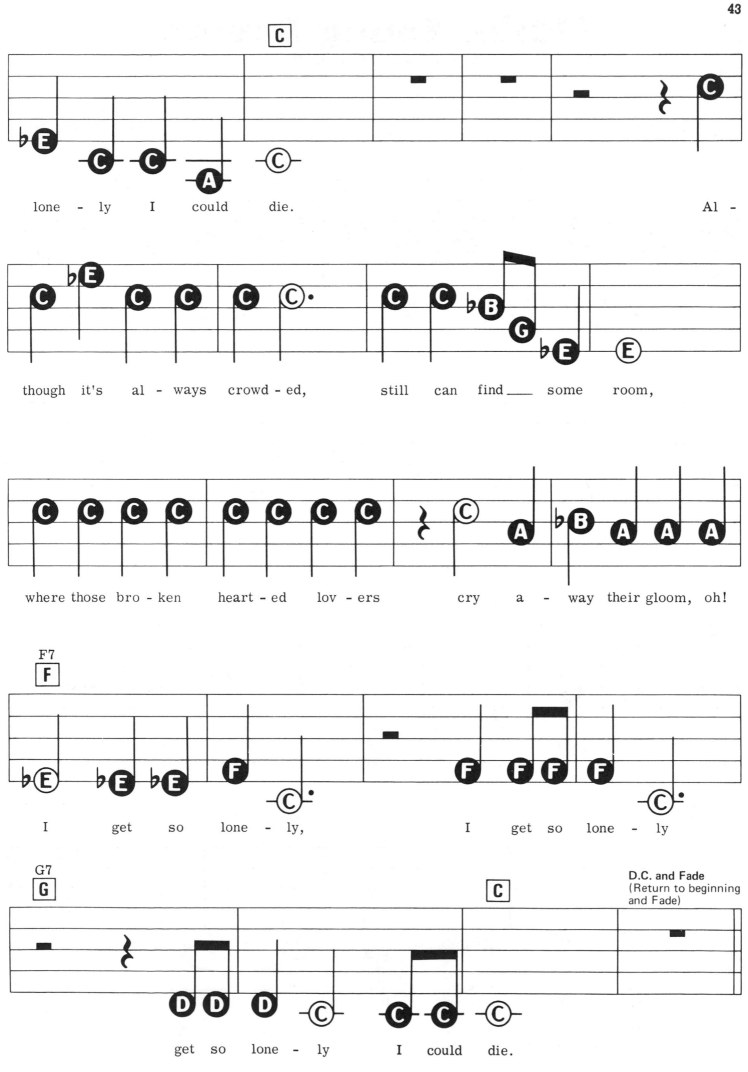

Hello, Young Lovers

from THE KING AND I

Registration 1
Rhythm: Waltz

Lyrics by Oscar Hammerstein II
Music by Richard Rodgers

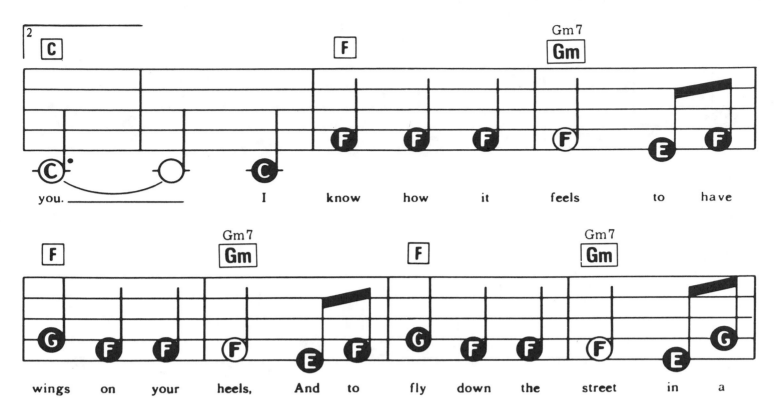

you. _____ I know how it feels to have

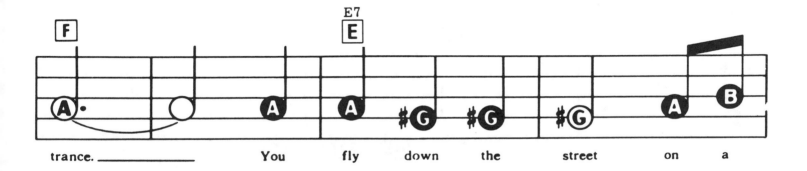

wings on your heels, And to fly down the street in a

trance. _____ You fly down the street on a

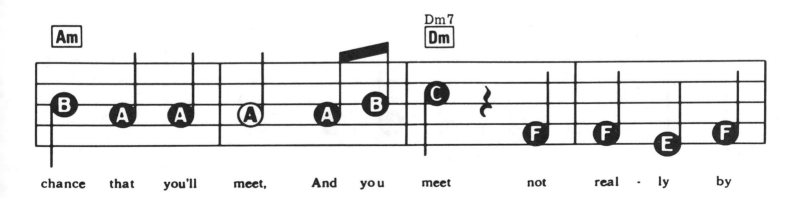

chance that you'll meet, And you meet not real - ly by

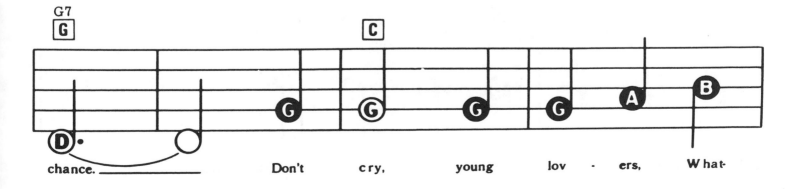

chance. _____ Don't cry, young lov - ers, What-

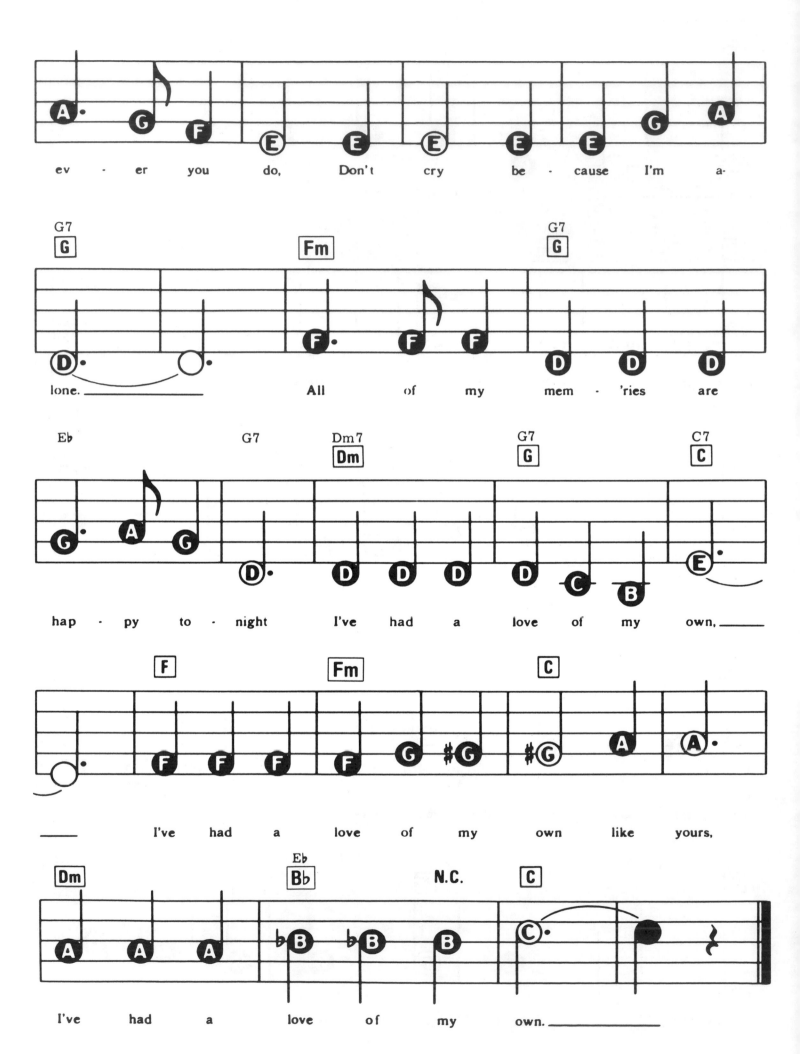

I Believe

Registration 2
Rhythm: Ballad or Slow Rock

Words and Music by Ervin Drake,
Irvin Graham, Jimmy Shirl and Al Stillman

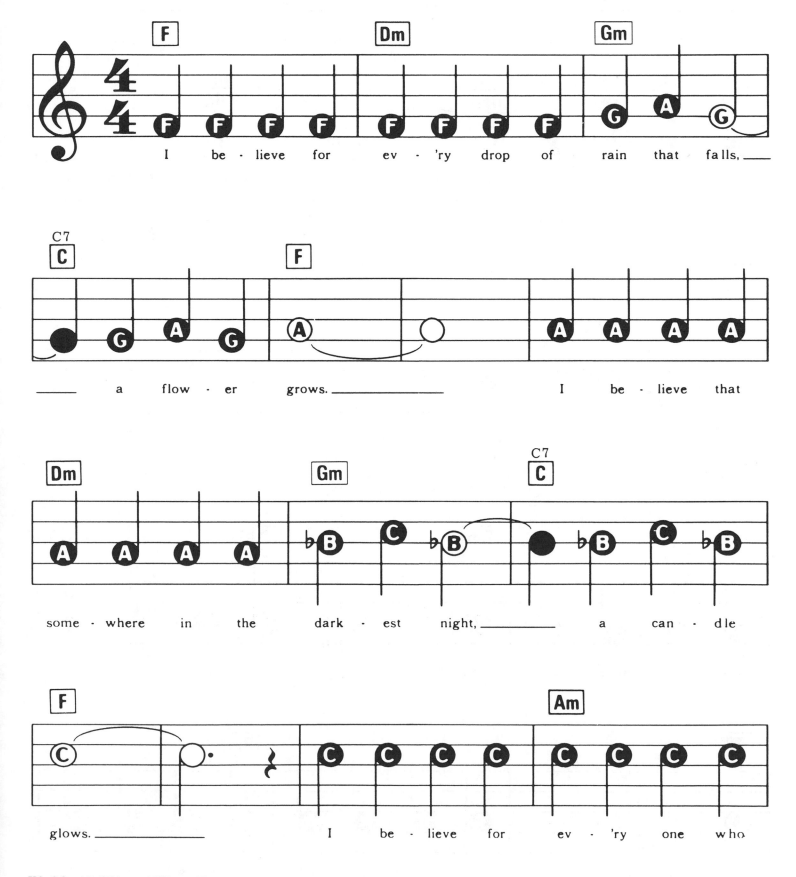

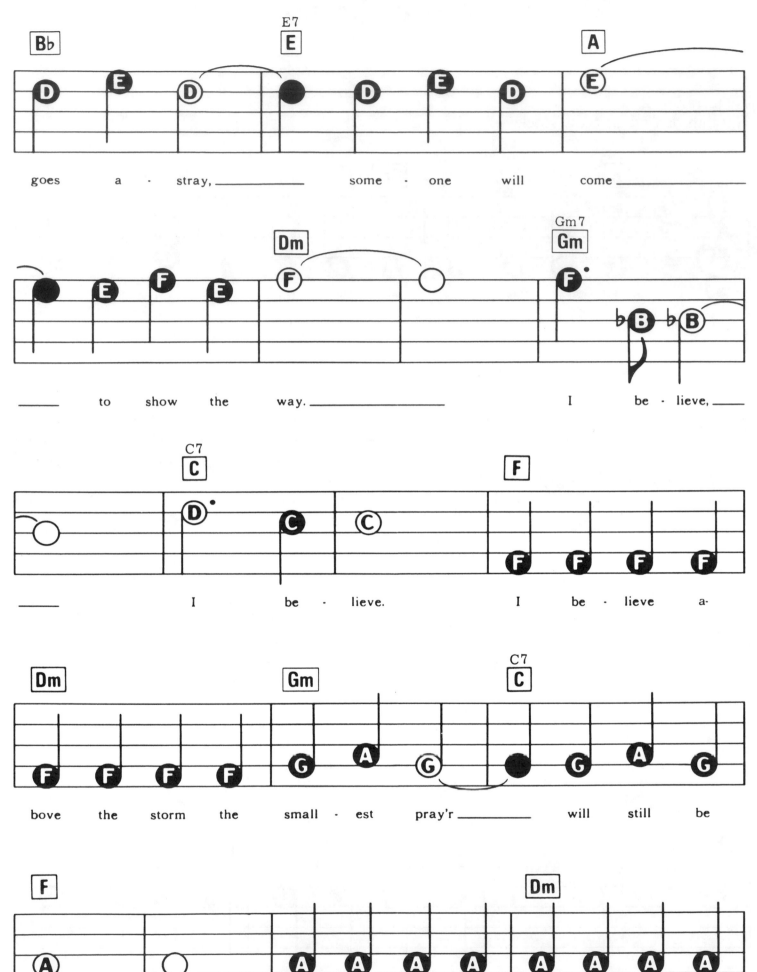

goes a - stray, _____ some - one will come _____

_____ to show the way. _____ I be - lieve, _____

_____ I be - lieve. I be - lieve a-

bove the storm the small - est pray'r _____ will still be

heard. _____ I be - lieve that some - one in the

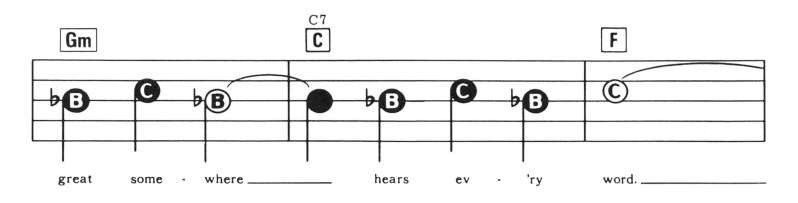

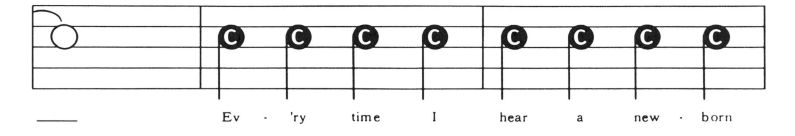

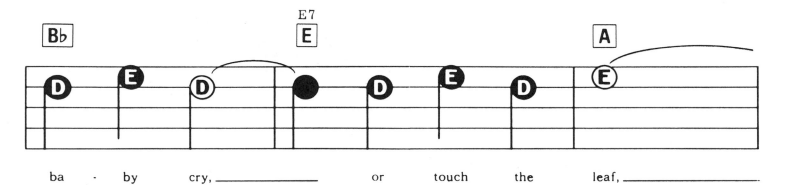

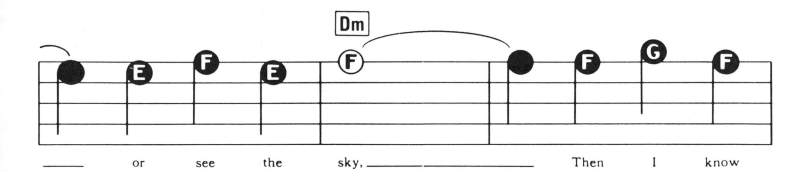

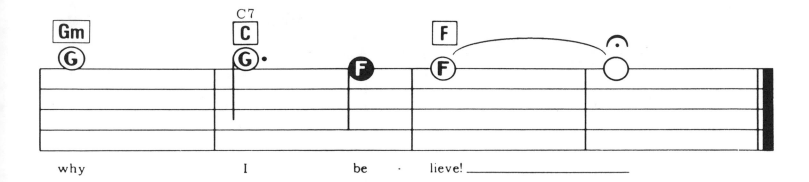

Here's That Rainy Day
from CARNIVAL IN FLANDERS

Registration 2
Rhythm: Ballad or Slow Rock

Words and Music by
Johnny Burke and James Van Heusen

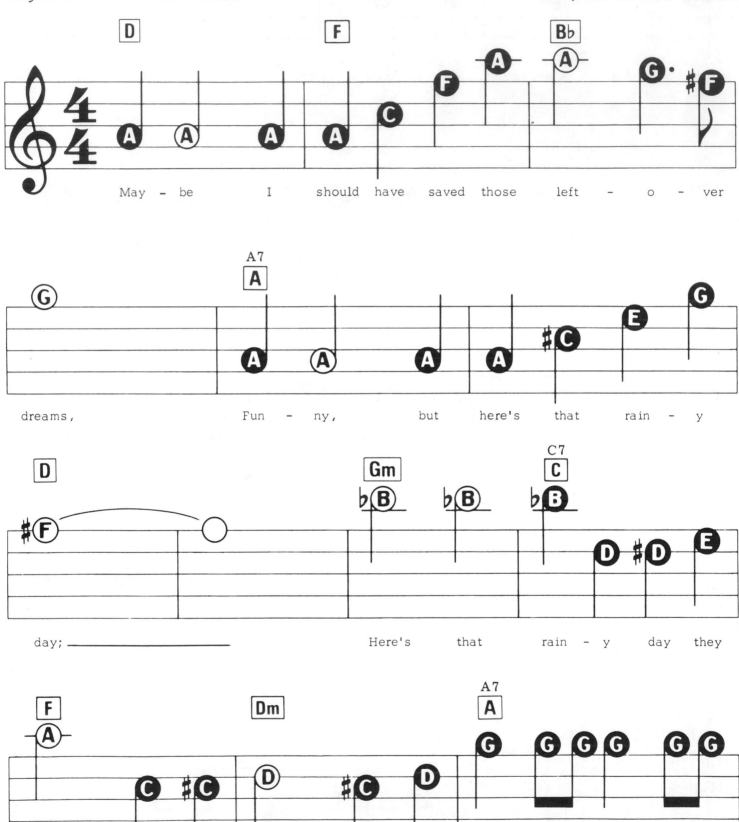

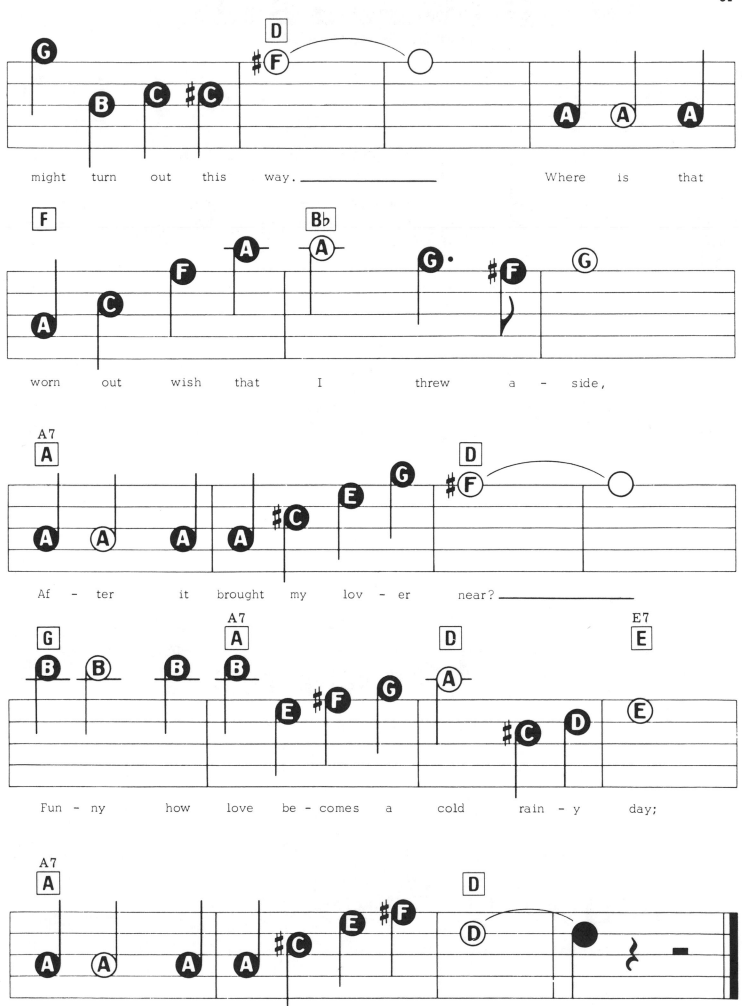

If I Were a Bell
from GUYS AND DOLLS

Registration 1
Rhythm: Fox Trot or Swing

By Frank Loesser

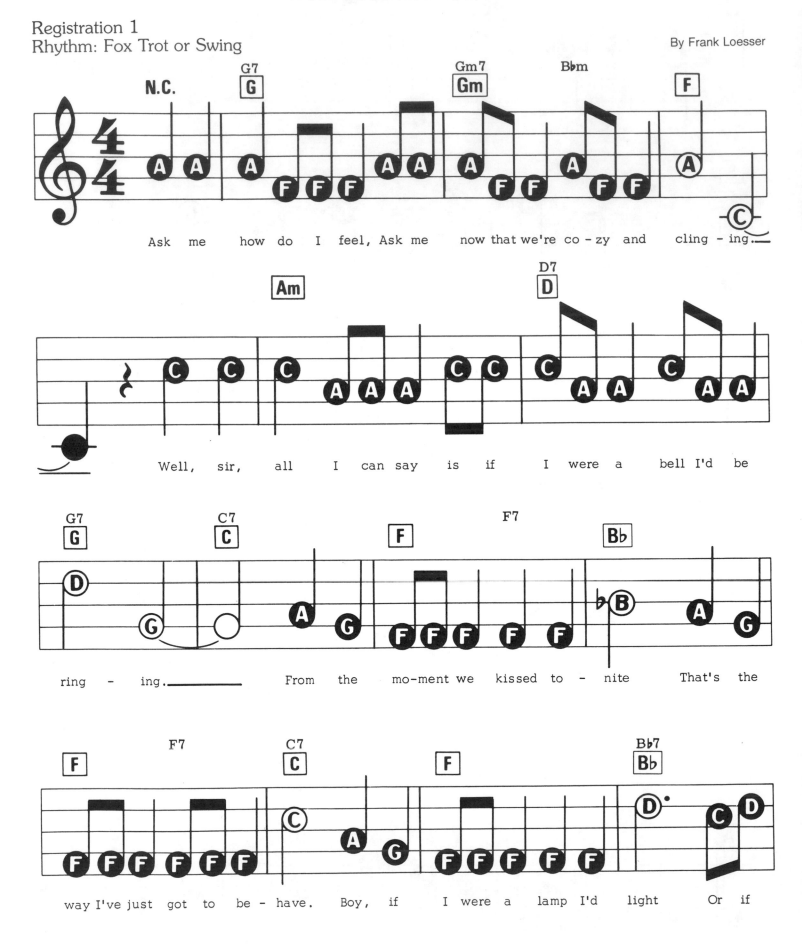

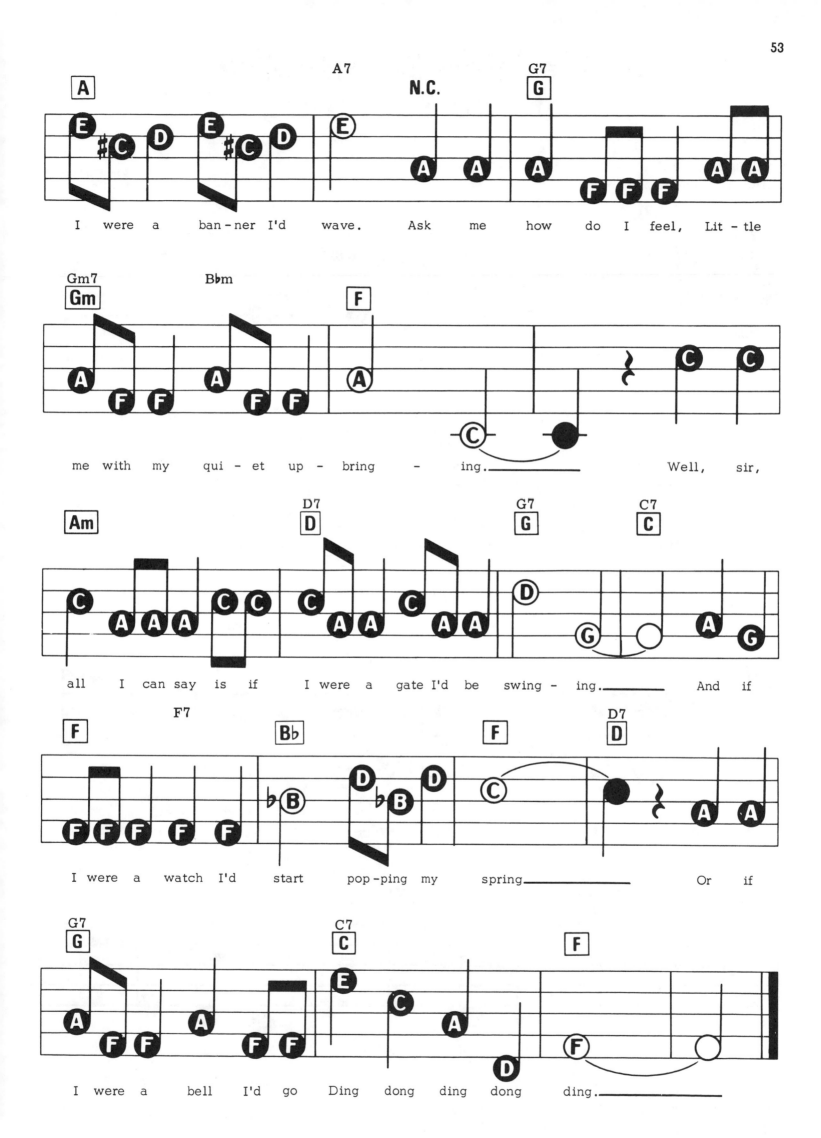

In the Wee Small Hours of the Morning

Registration 2
Rhythm: Ballad or Fox Trot

Words by Bob Hilliard
Music by David Mann

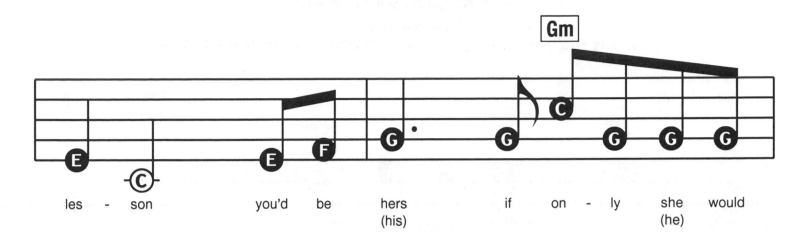

les - son you'd be hers if on - ly she would
(his) (he)

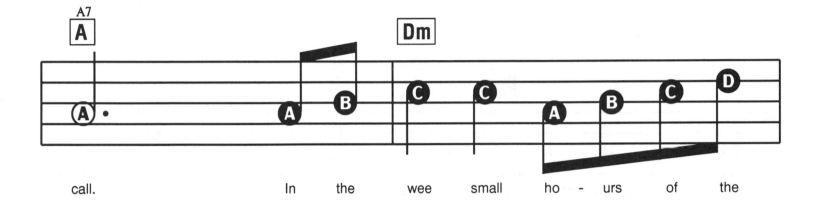

call. In the wee small ho - urs of the

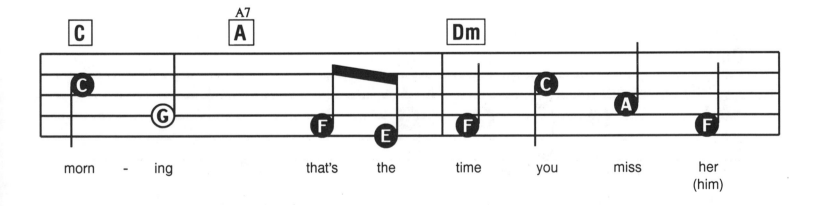

morn - ing that's the time you miss her
(him)

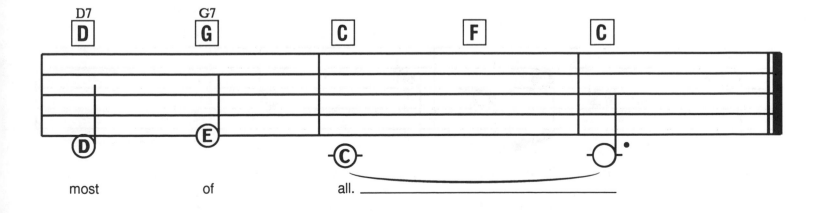

most of all. _____

Innamorata
(Sweetheart)
from the Paramount Picture ARTISTS AND MODELS

Registration 3
Rhythm: Waltz

Words by Jack Brooks
Music by Harry Warren

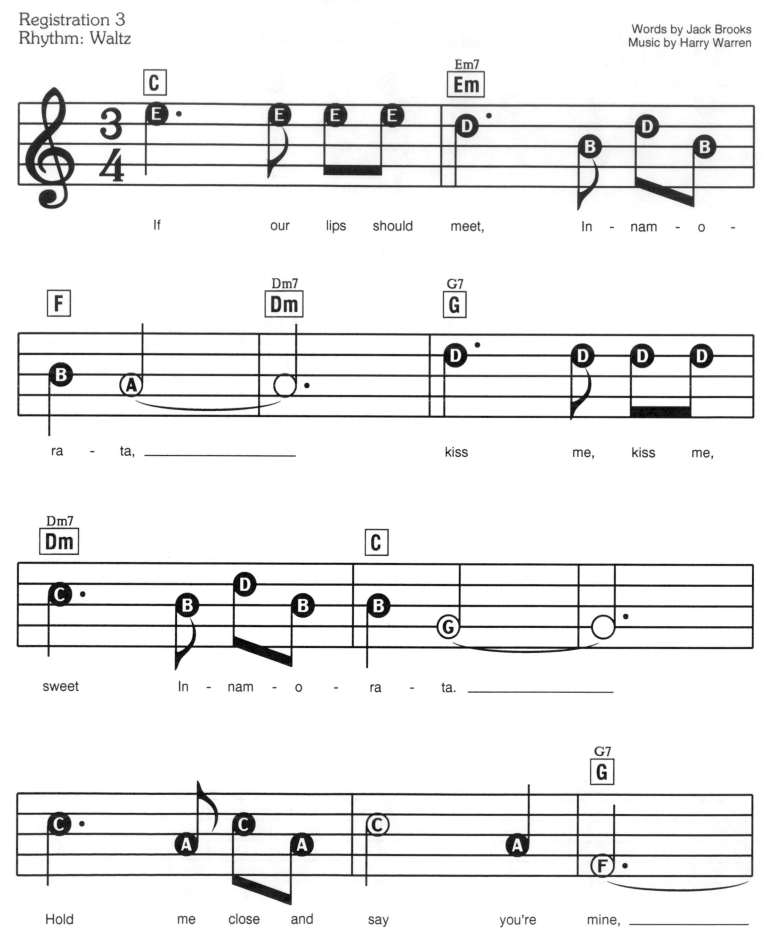

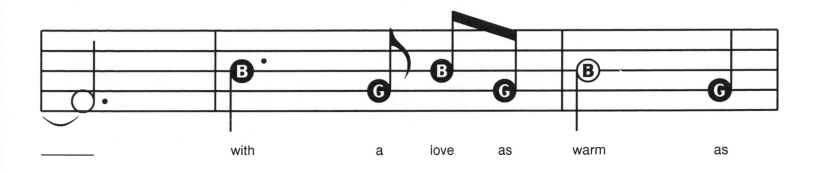

_____ with a love as warm as

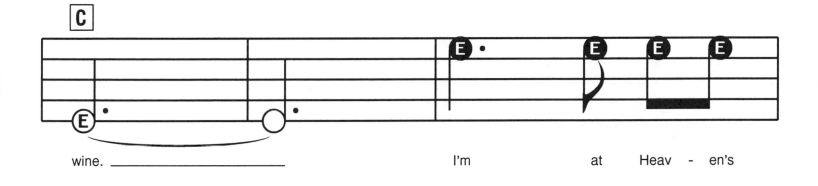

wine. _____ I'm at Heav - en's

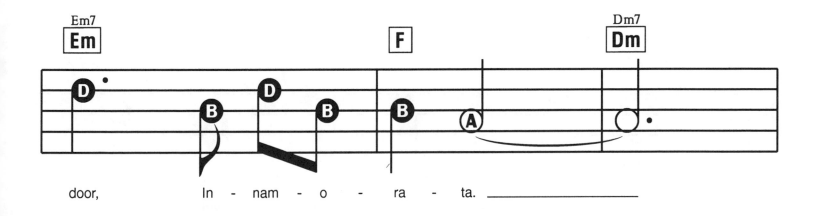

door, In - nam - o - ra - ta. _____

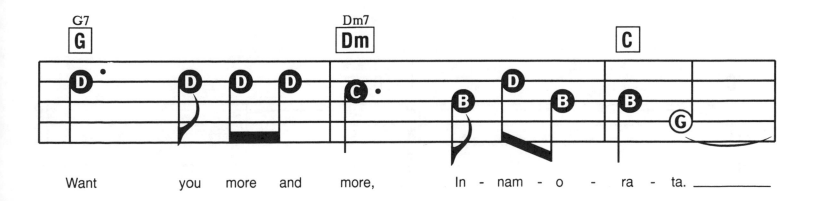

Want you more and more, In - nam - o - ra - ta. _____

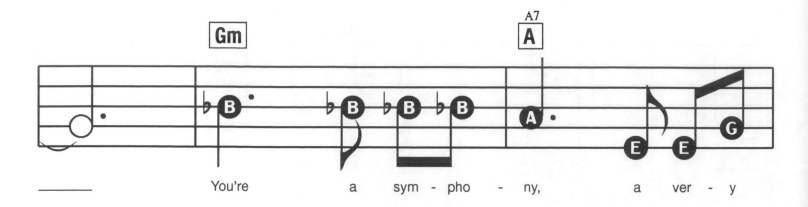

You're   a   sym - pho - ny,   a   ver - y

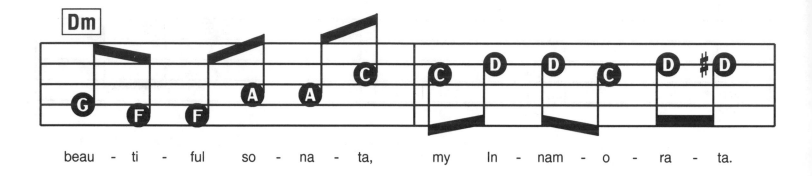

beau - ti - ful so - na - ta,   my In - nam - o - ra - ta.

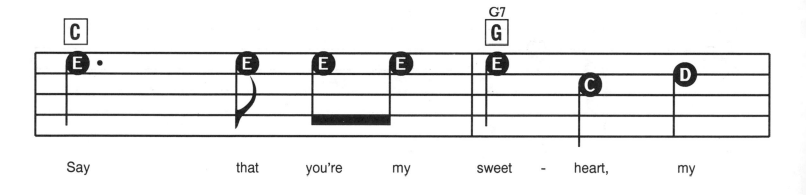

Say   that   you're   my   sweet - heart,   my

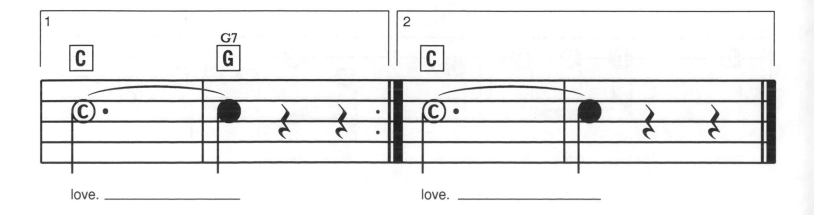

love. _____   love. _____

Luck Be a Lady
from GUYS AND DOLLS

Registration 4
Rhythm: Fox Trot or Swing

By Frank Loesser

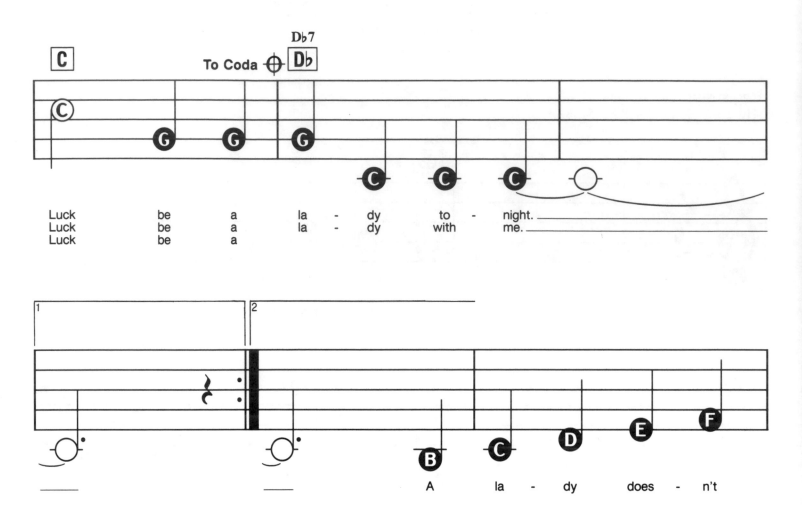

Luck be a la - dy to - night.
Luck be a a la - dy with me.
Luck be a

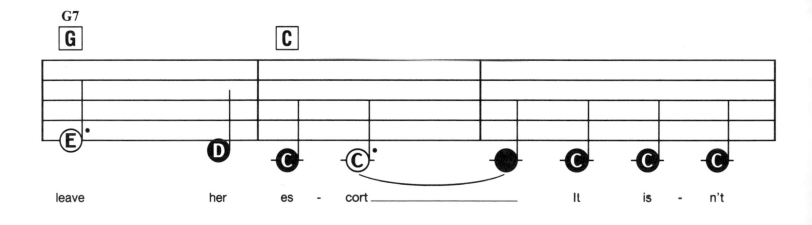

A la - dy does - n't

leave her es - cort It is - n't

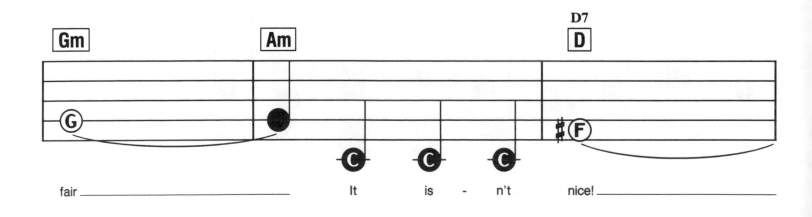

fair It is - n't nice!

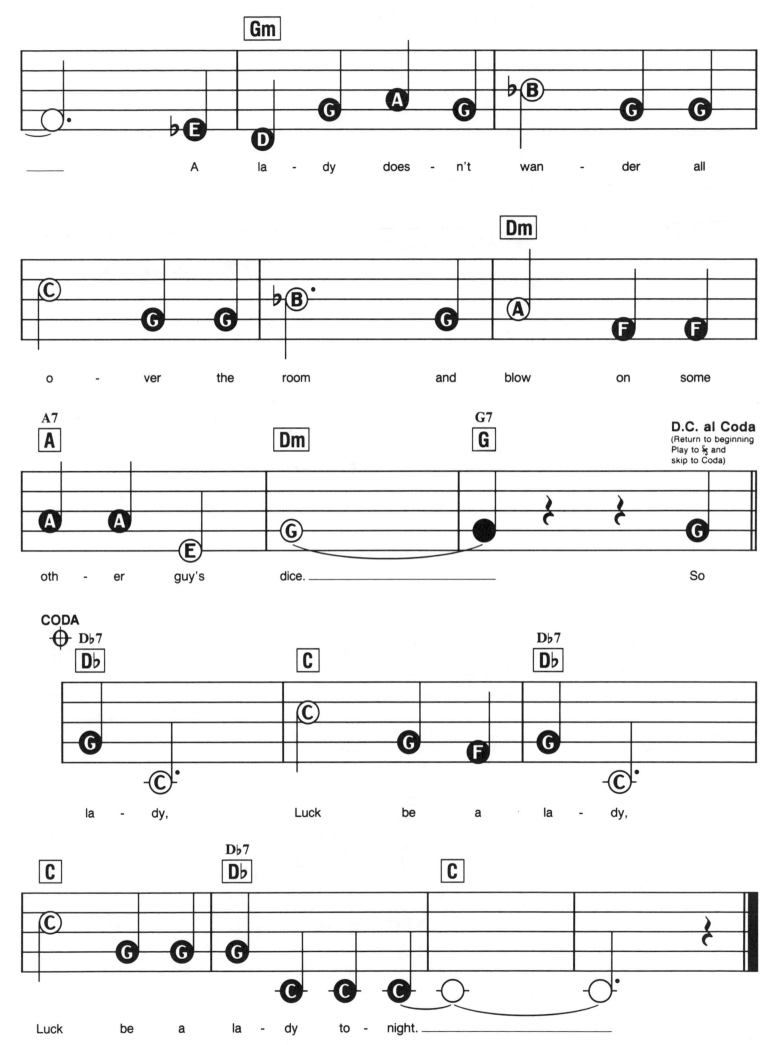

Johnny B. Goode

Registration 4
Rhythm: Rock or Swing

Words and Music by
Chuck Berry

Let It Be Me
(Je T'appartiens)

English Words by Mann Curtis
French Words by Pierre DeLanoe
Music by Gilbert Becaud

Registration 5
Rhythm: Fox Trot or Swing

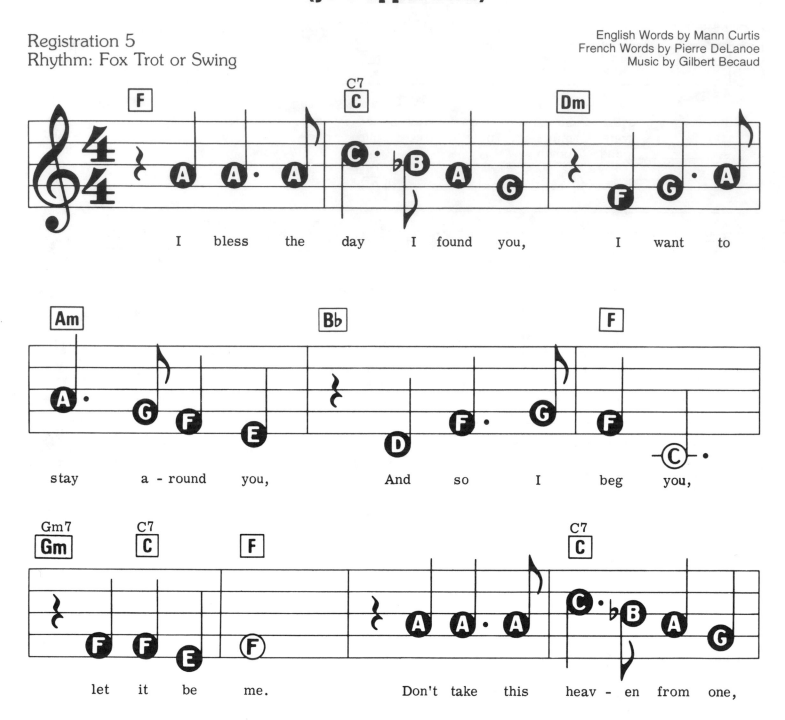

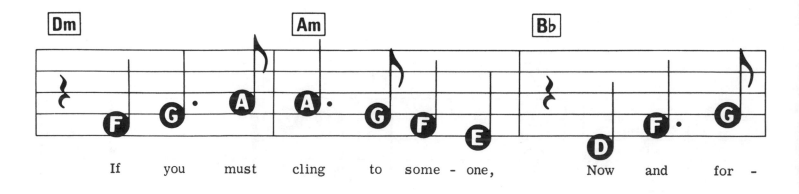

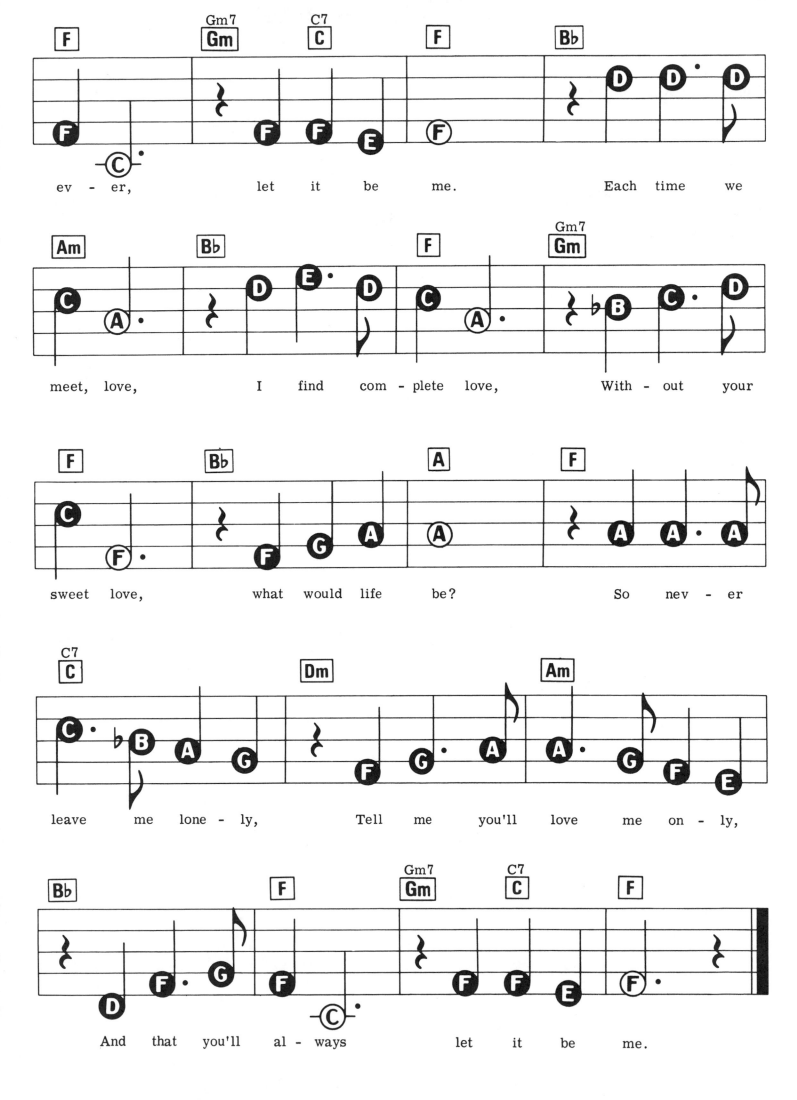

Love Me Tender

Registration 9
Rhythm: Slow Rock or Rock

Words and Music by
Elvis Presley and Vera Matson

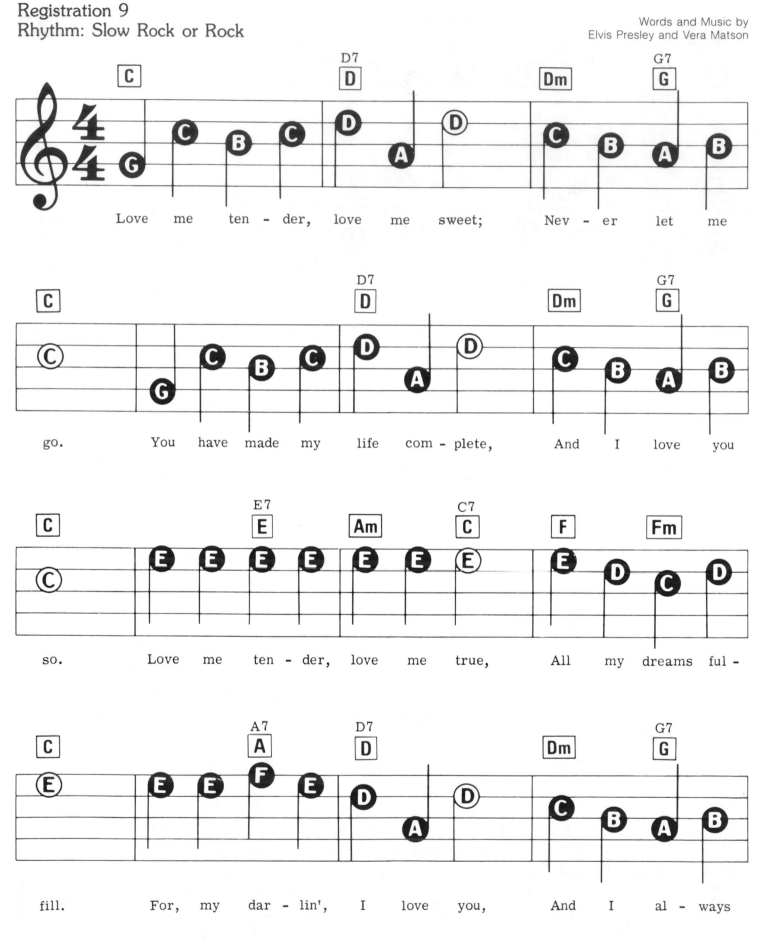

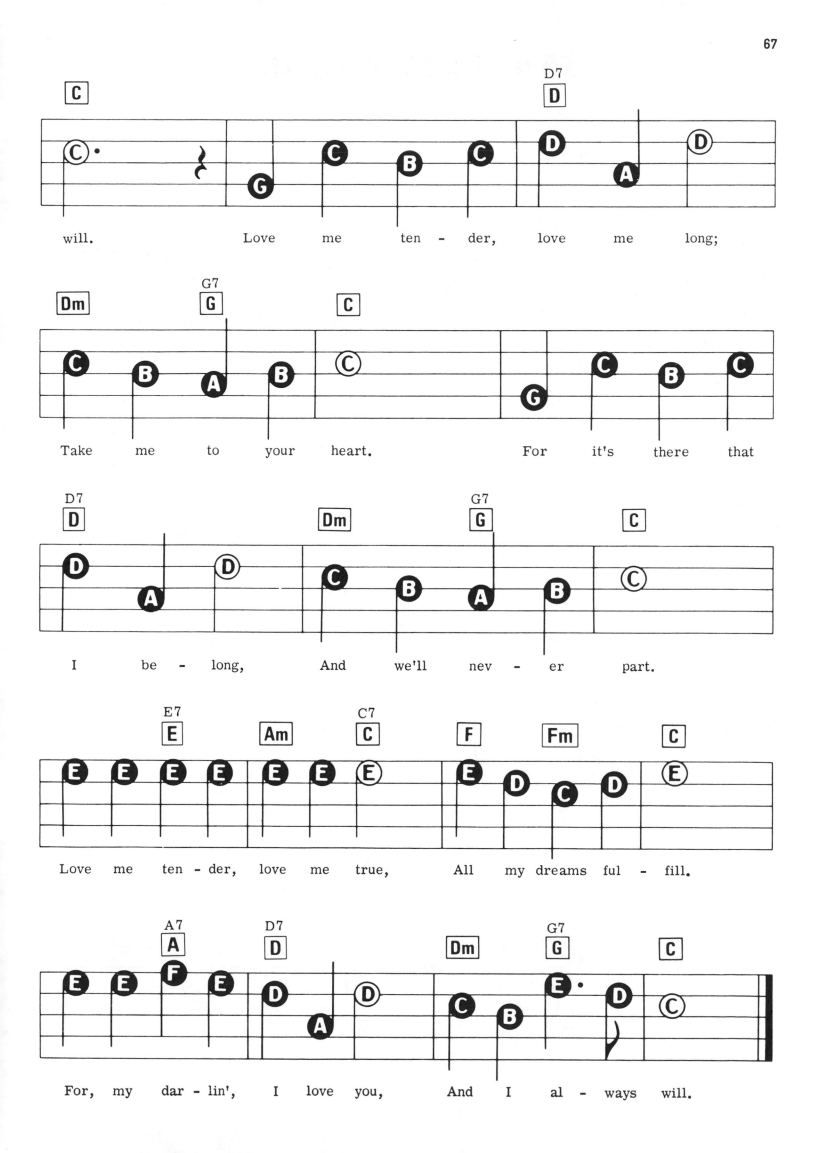

Magic Moments

Registration 9
Rhythm: Swing or Shuffle

Lyric by Hal David
Music by Burt Bacharach

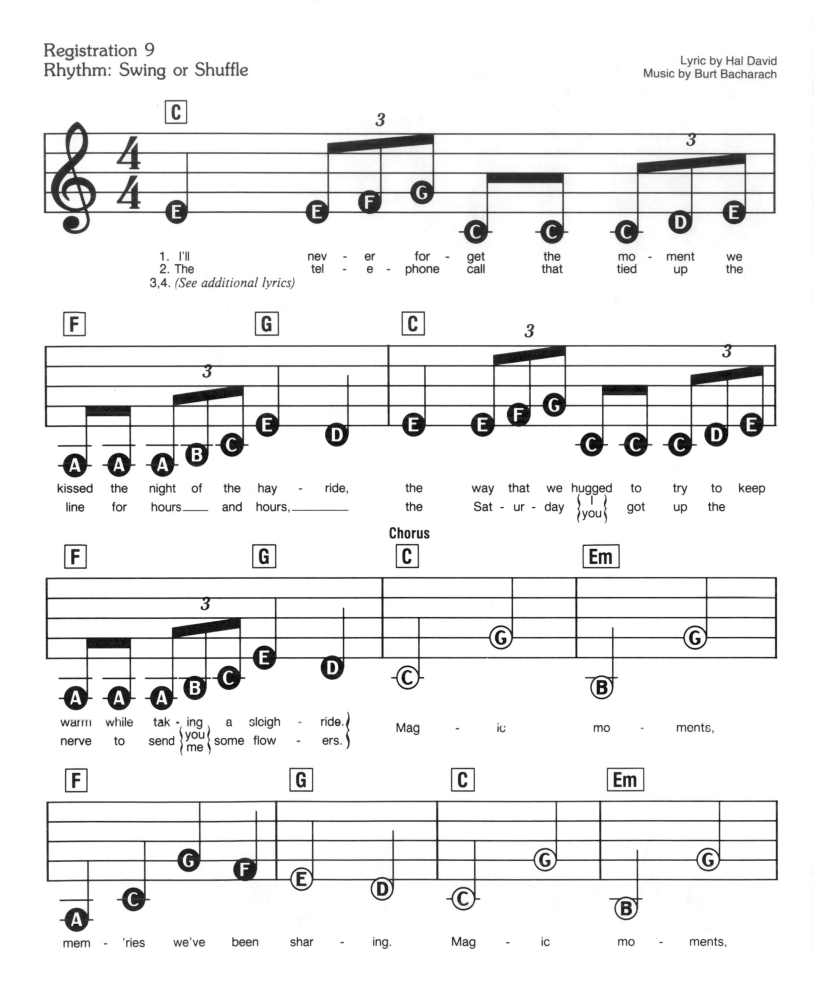

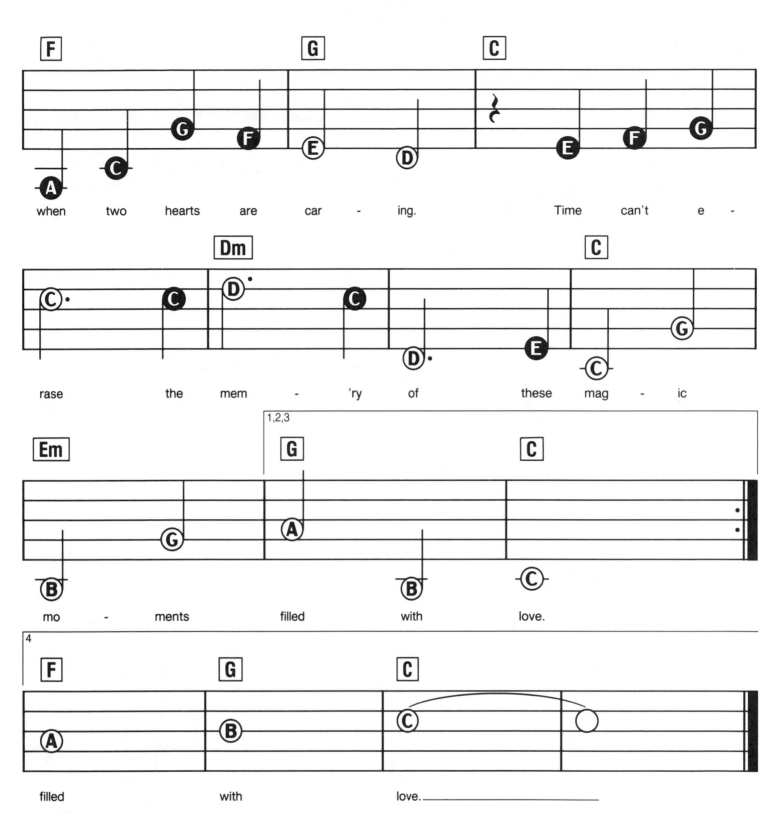

when two hearts are car - ing. Time can't e -

rase the mem - 'ry of these mag - ic

mo - ments filled with love.

filled with love.

Additional Lyrics

3. The way that we cheered whenever our team was scoring a touchdown,
   The time that the floor fell out of { my / your } car when { I / you } put the clutch down;
   (To Chorus)

4. The penny arcade, the games that we played, the fun and the prizes,
   The Halloween hop when ev'ryone came in funny disguises;
   (To Chorus)

Misty

Registration 8
Rhythm: Swing or Jazz

Words by Johnny Burke
Music by Erroll Garner

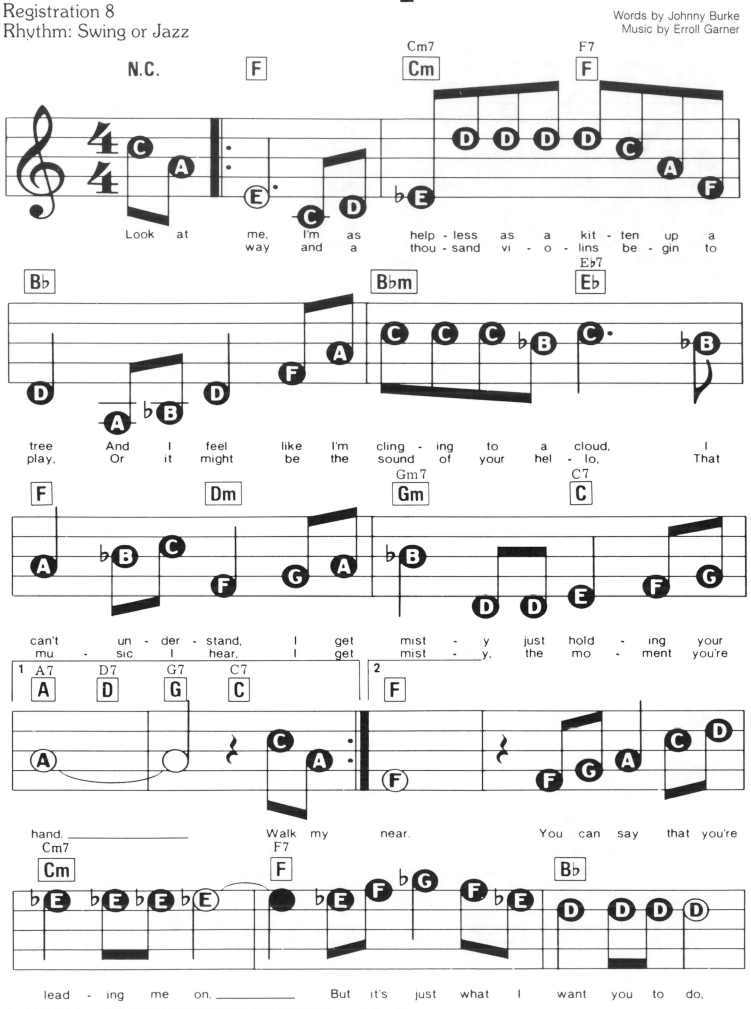

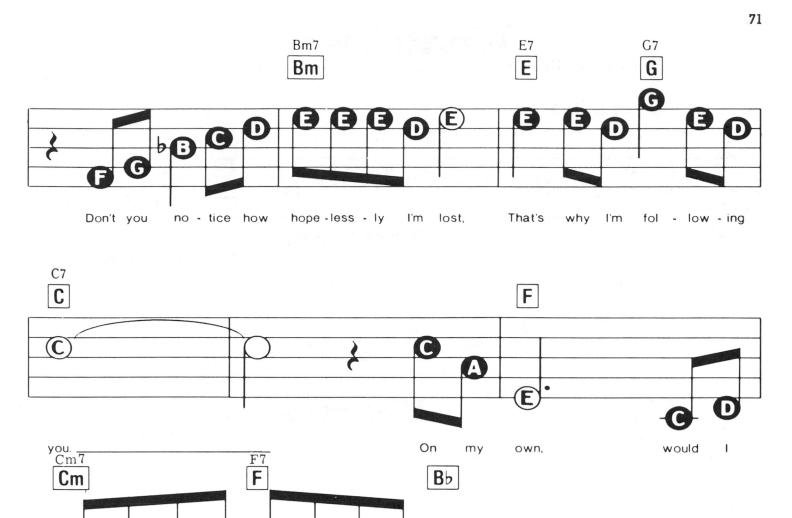

Don't you no-tice how hope-less-ly I'm lost, That's why I'm fol-low-ing

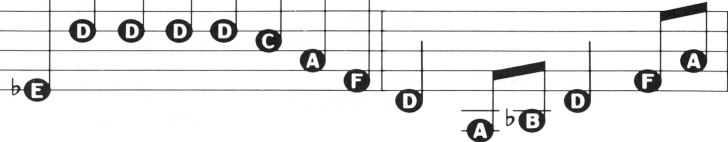

you. On my own, would I

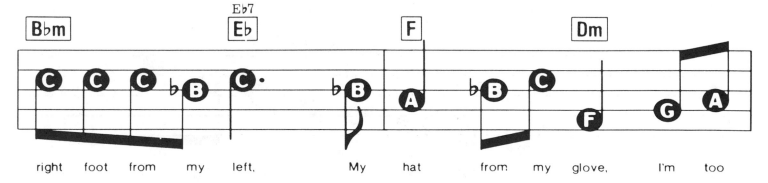

wan-der through this won-der land a-lone, Nev-er know-ing my

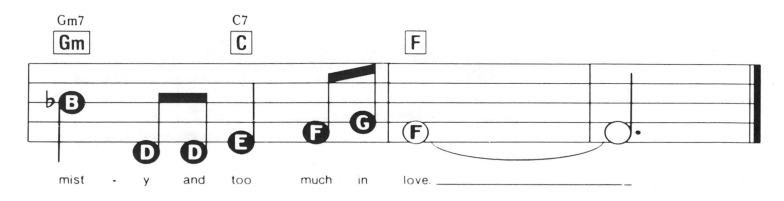

right foot from my left, My hat from my glove, I'm too

mist - y and too much in love. _____

Mona Lisa
from the Paramount Picture CAPTAIN CAREY, U.S.A.

Registration 9
Rhythm: Swing or 8 Beat

Words and Music by Jay Livingston
and Ray Evans

N.C.

D #C | G E D D #C E D B G

Mo - na Li - sa, Mo - na Li - sa, men have

E D | G #F | #F E E D D B C D

named you. You're so like the la - dy with the mys - tic

Am

A E #D | #F E C B D C A #G

smile. Is it on - ly 'cause you're lone - ly they have

D7
D

B A D E #F G A B C E D C

blamed you for that Mo - na Li - sa strange - ness in your

G

B D #C | E D D #C E D B G

smile? Do you smile to tempt a lov - er, Mo - na

My Favorite Things
from THE SOUND OF MUSIC

Registration 9
Rhythm: Waltz

Lyrics by Oscar Hammerstein II
Music by Richard Rodgers

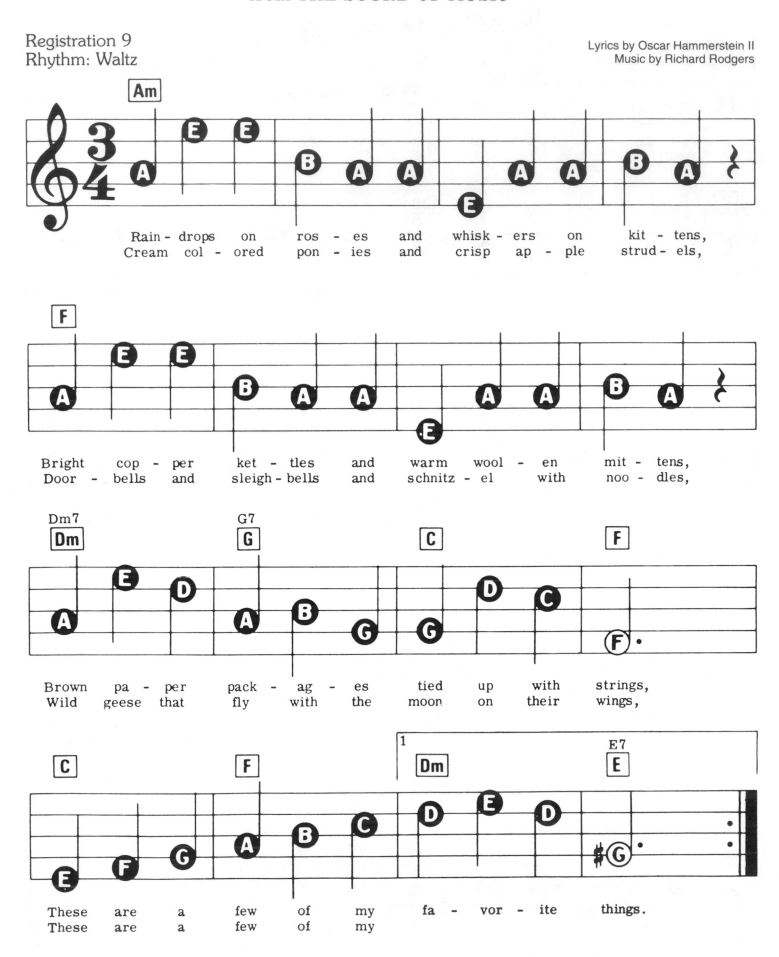

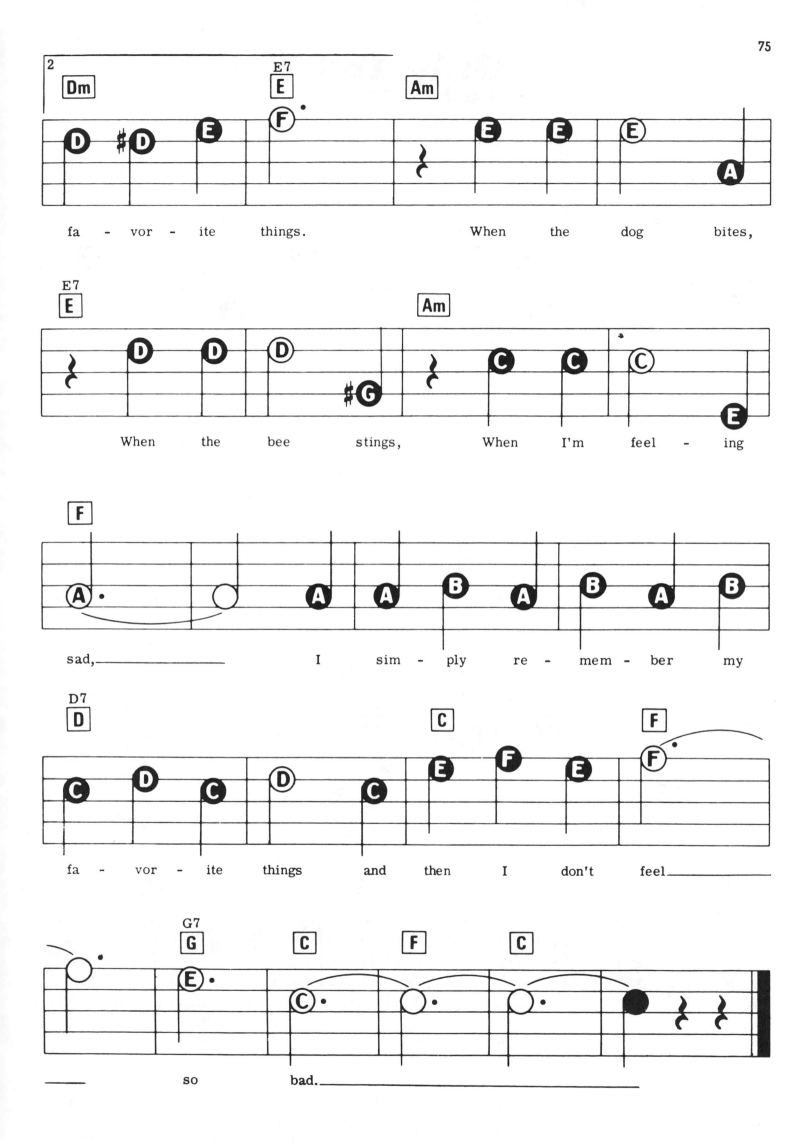

Only You
(And You Alone)

Registration 2
Rhythm: Swing

Words and Music by
Buck Ram and Ande Rand

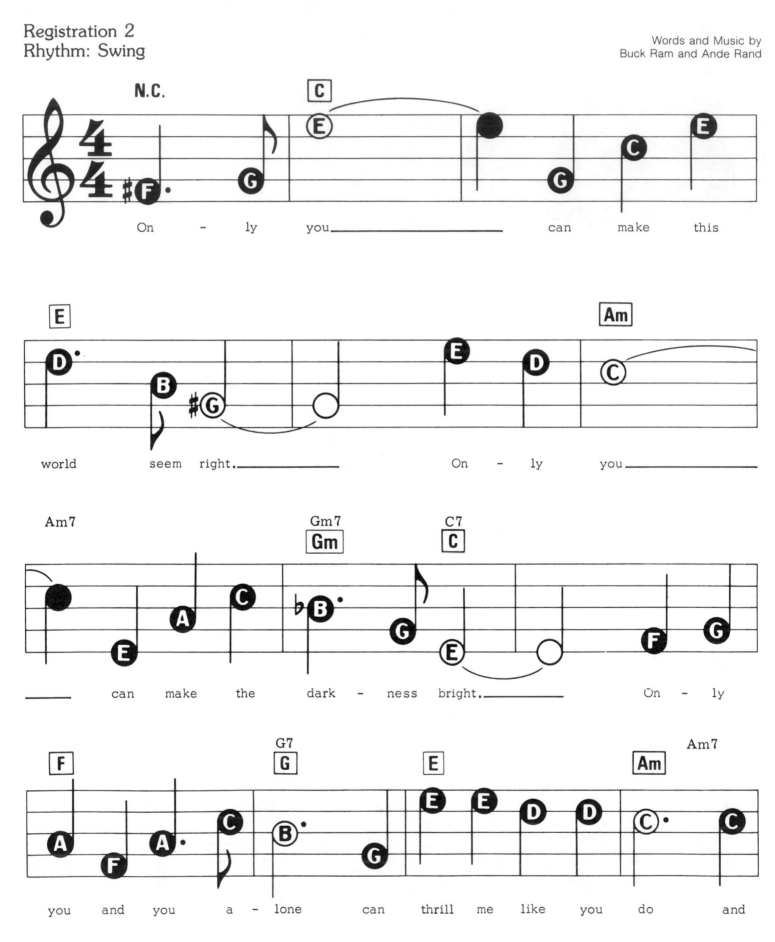

77

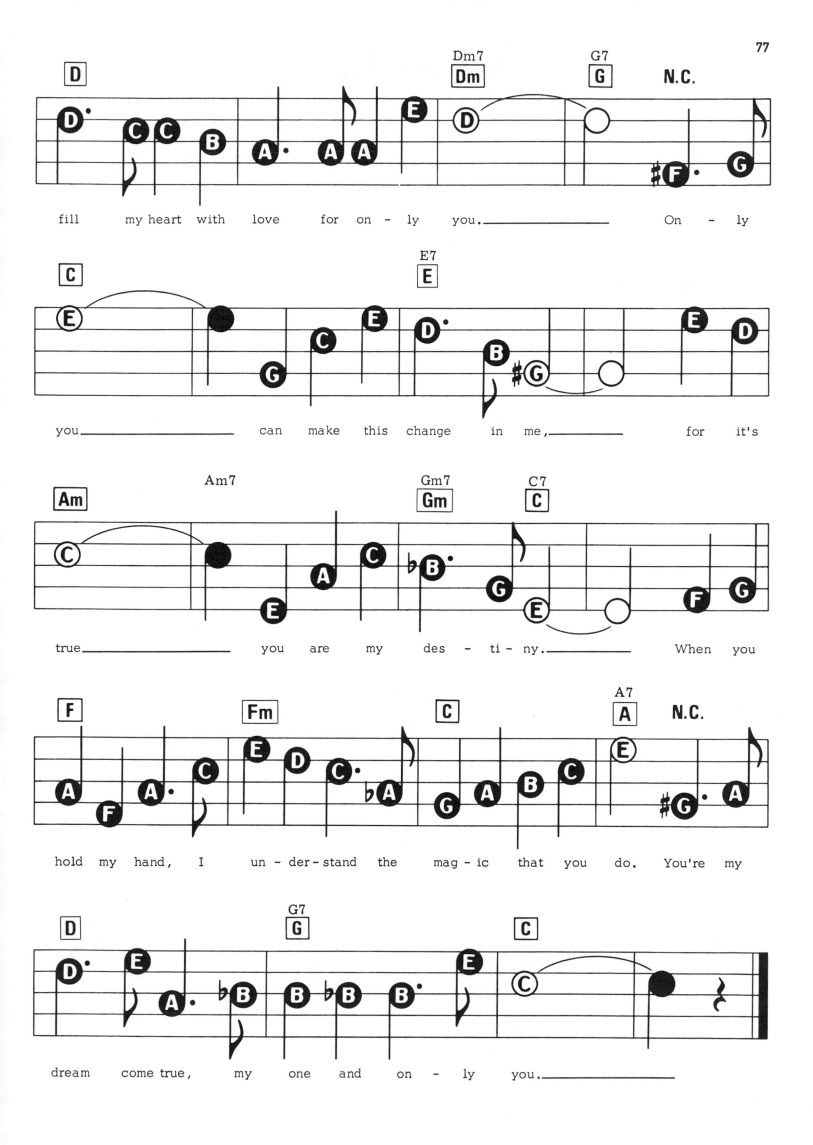

Peggy Sue
from THE BUDDY HOLLY STORY

Registration 3
Rhythm: Rock

Words and Music by Jerry Allison,
Norman Petty and Buddy Holly

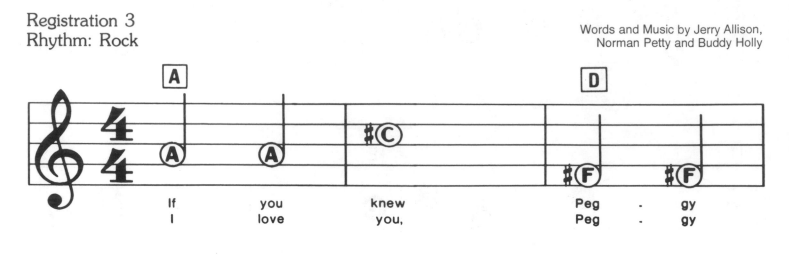

If   you   knew   you,   Peg - gy
I   love   you,   Peg - gy

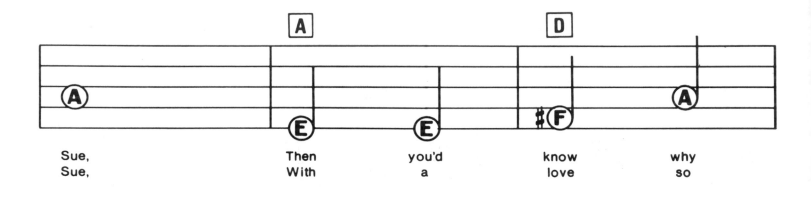

Sue,   Then   you'd   know   why
Sue,   With   a   love   so

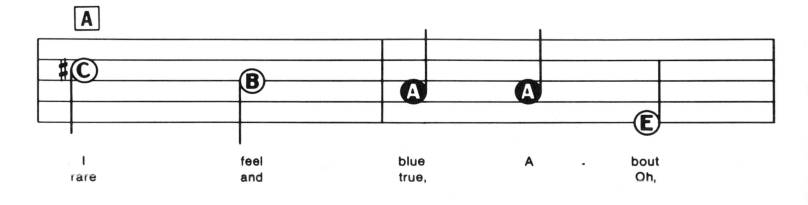

I   feel   blue   A - bout
rare   and   true,   Oh,

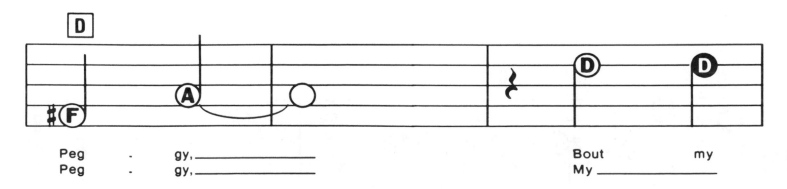

Peg - gy,_____   Bout   my
Peg - gy,_____   My _____

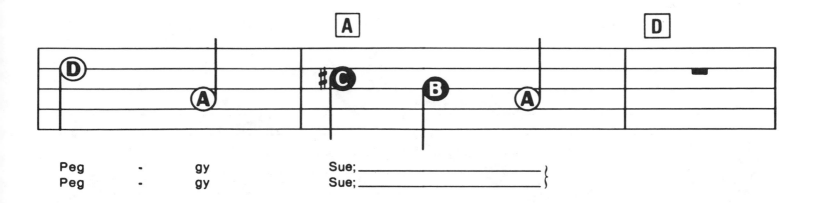

Peg - gy Sue;_____
Peg - gy Sue;_____

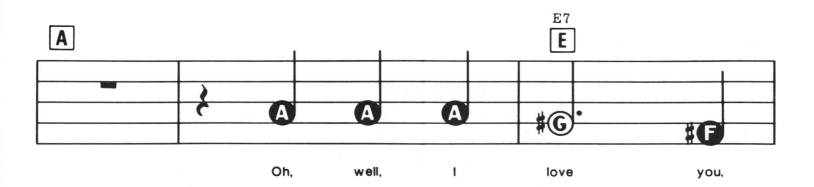

Oh, well, I love you,

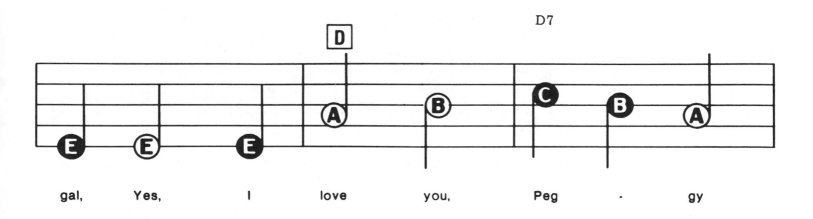

gal, Yes, I love you, Peg - gy

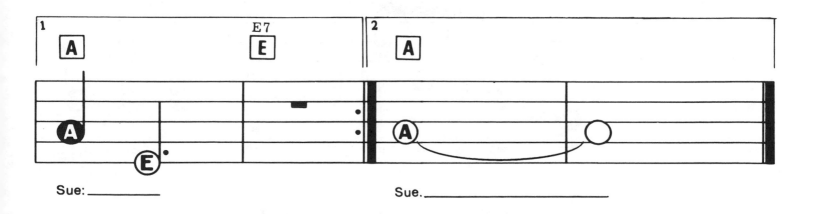

Sue:_____   Sue._____

P.S. I Love You

Registration 2
Rhythm: Swing or Fox Trot

Words by Johnny Mercer
Music by Gordon Jenkins

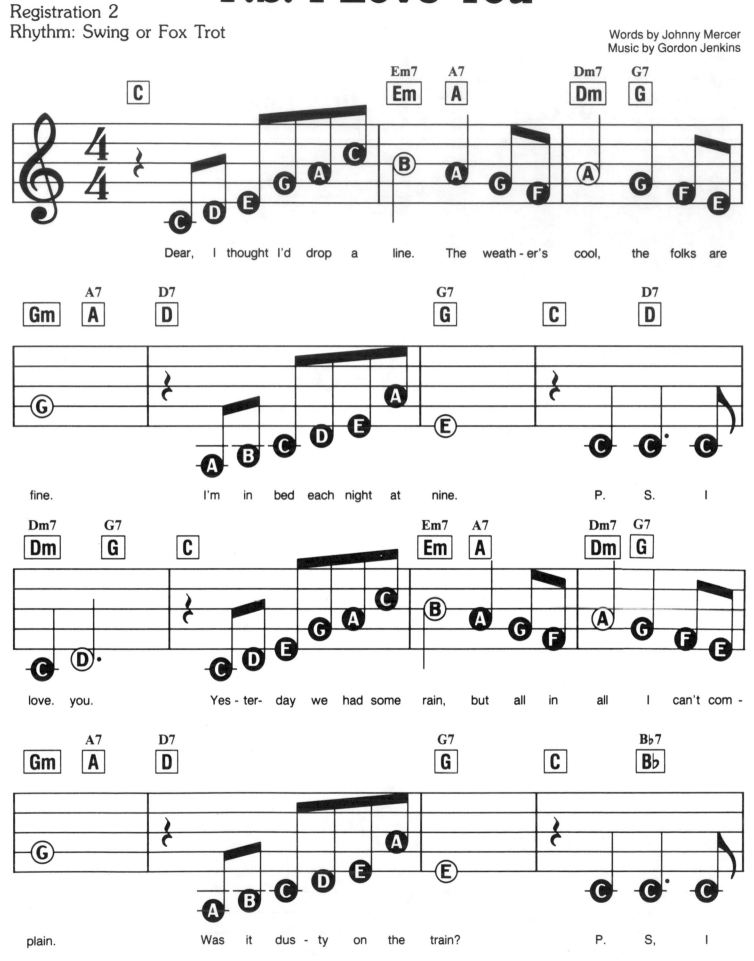

MCA music publishing

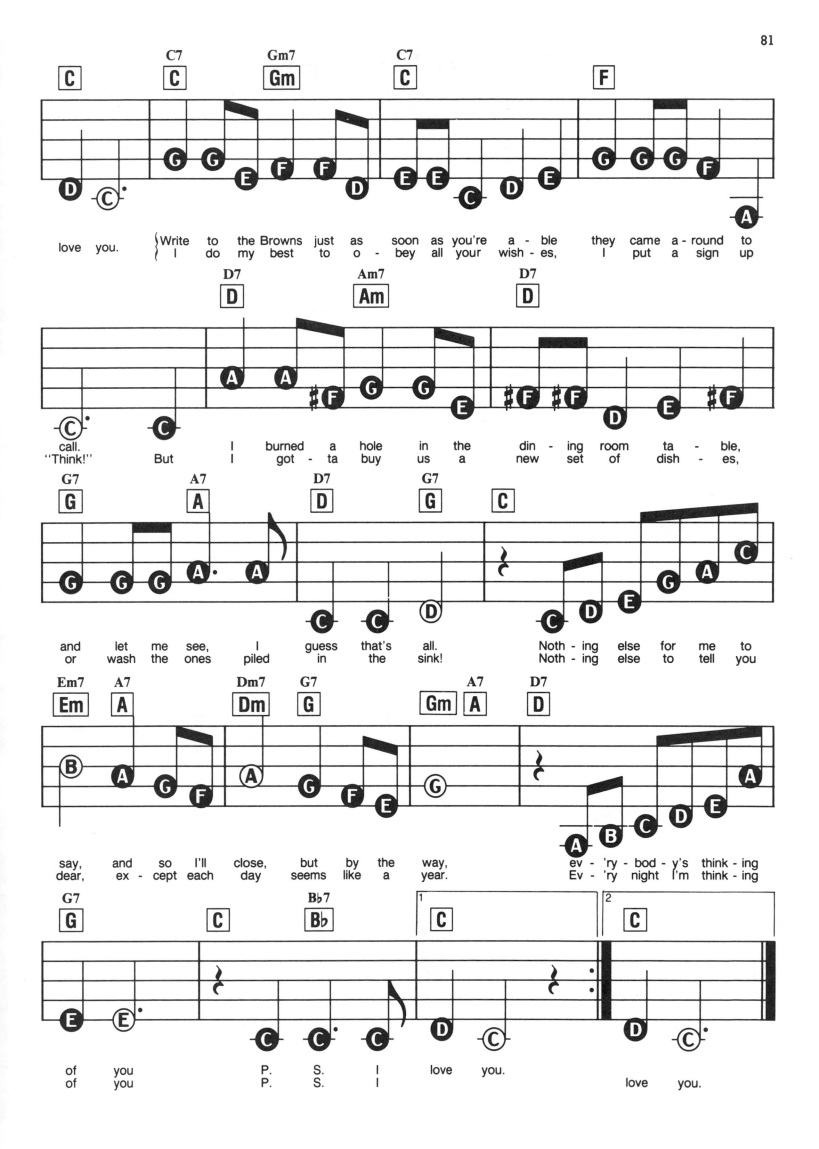

Que Sera, Sera
(Whatever Will Be, Will Be)
from THE MAN WHO KNEW TOO MUCH

Registration 10
Rhythm: Waltz

Words and Music by
Jay Livingston and Ray Evans

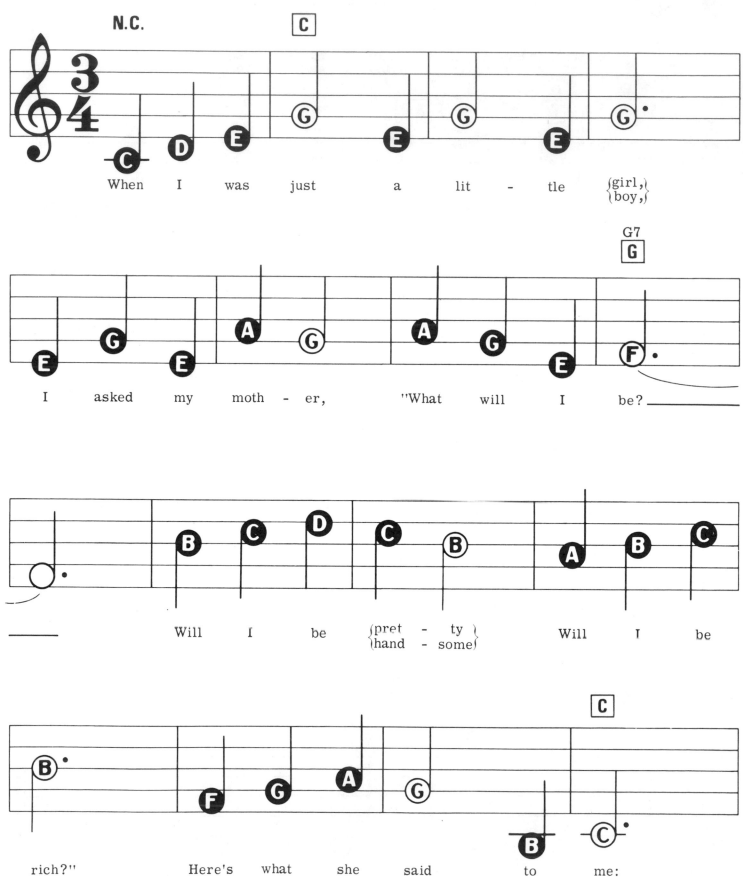

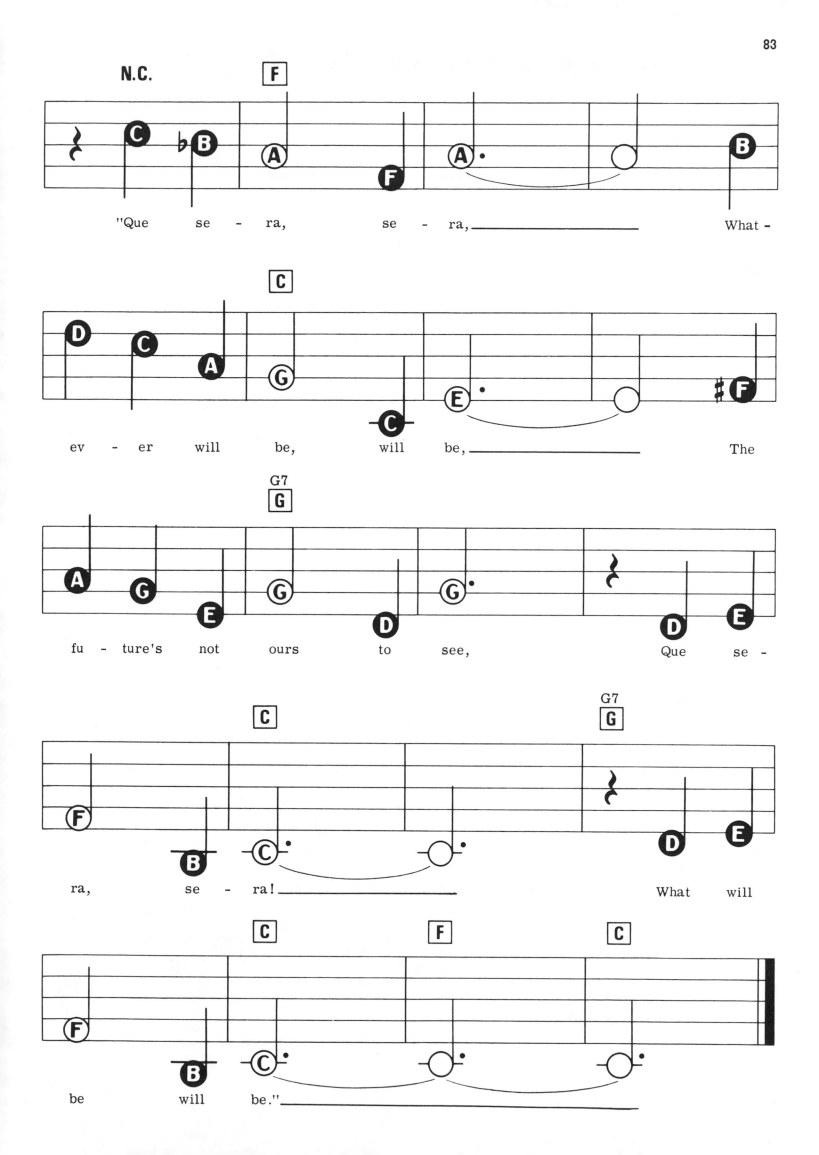

Rock Around the Clock

Registration 8
Rhythm: Rock

By Max C. Freedman and Jimmy DeKnight

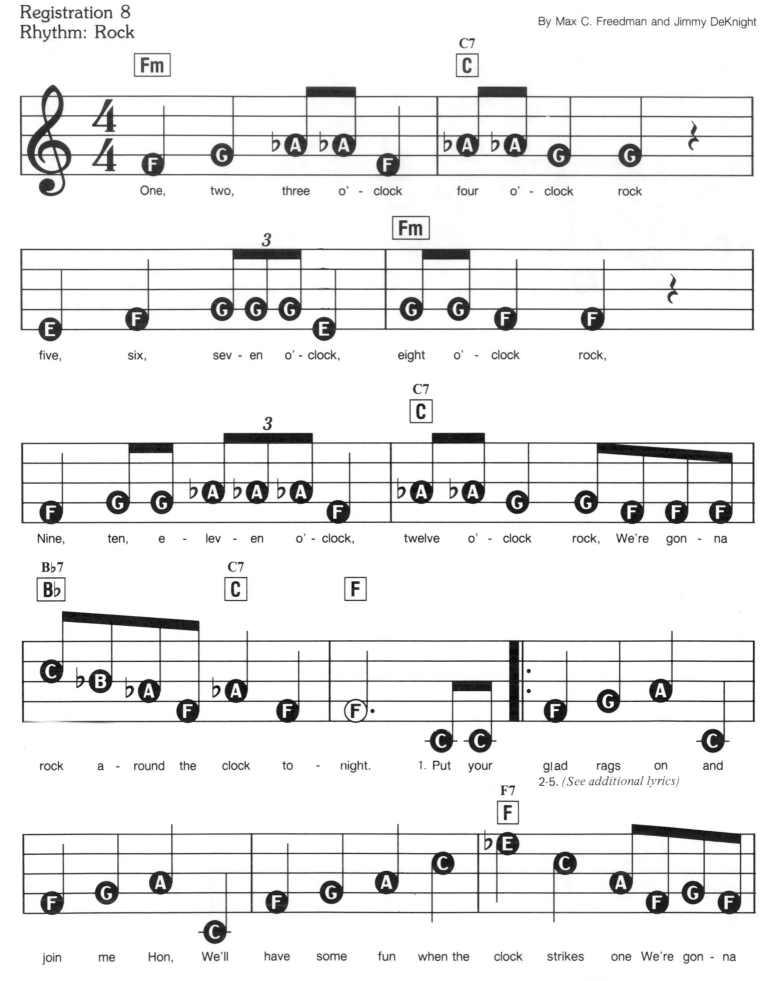

One, two, three o'-clock four o'-clock rock

five, six, sev-en o'-clock, eight o'-clock rock,

Nine, ten, e-lev-en o'-clock, twelve o'-clock rock, We're gon-na

rock a-round the clock to - night. 1. Put your glad rags on and
2-5. *(See additional lyrics)*

join me Hon, We'll have some fun when the clock strikes one We're gon-na

85

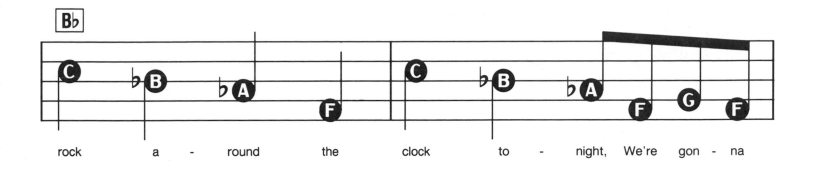

rock a - round the clock to - night, We're gon - na

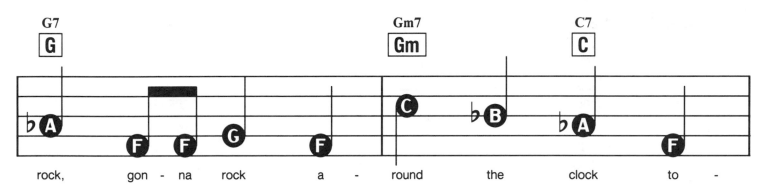

rock, rock, rock, 'til broad day - light, We're gon - na

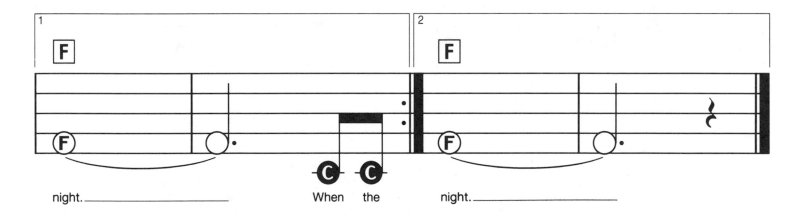

rock, gon - na rock a - round the clock to -

night._____ When the night._____

Additional Lyrics

2. When the clock strikes two, and three and four,
If the band slows down we'll yell for more,
We're gonna rock around the clock tonight,
We're gonna rock, rock, rock, etc....

3. When the chimes ring five and six and seven,
We'll be rockin' up in seventh heav'n,
We're gonna rock around the clock tonight,
We're gonna rock, rock, rock, etc....

4. When it's eight, nine, ten, eleven, too,
I'll be goin' strong and so will you,
We're gonna rock around the clock tonight,
We're gonna rock, rock, rock, etc....

5. When the clock strikes twelve, we'll cool off, then,
Start a rockin' 'round the clock again,
We're gonna rock around the clock tonight,
We're gonna rock, rock, rock, etc....

Satin Doll
from SOPHISTICATED LADIES

Registration 4
Rhythm: Swing or Jazz

By Duke Ellington, Johnny Mercer
and Billy Strayhorn

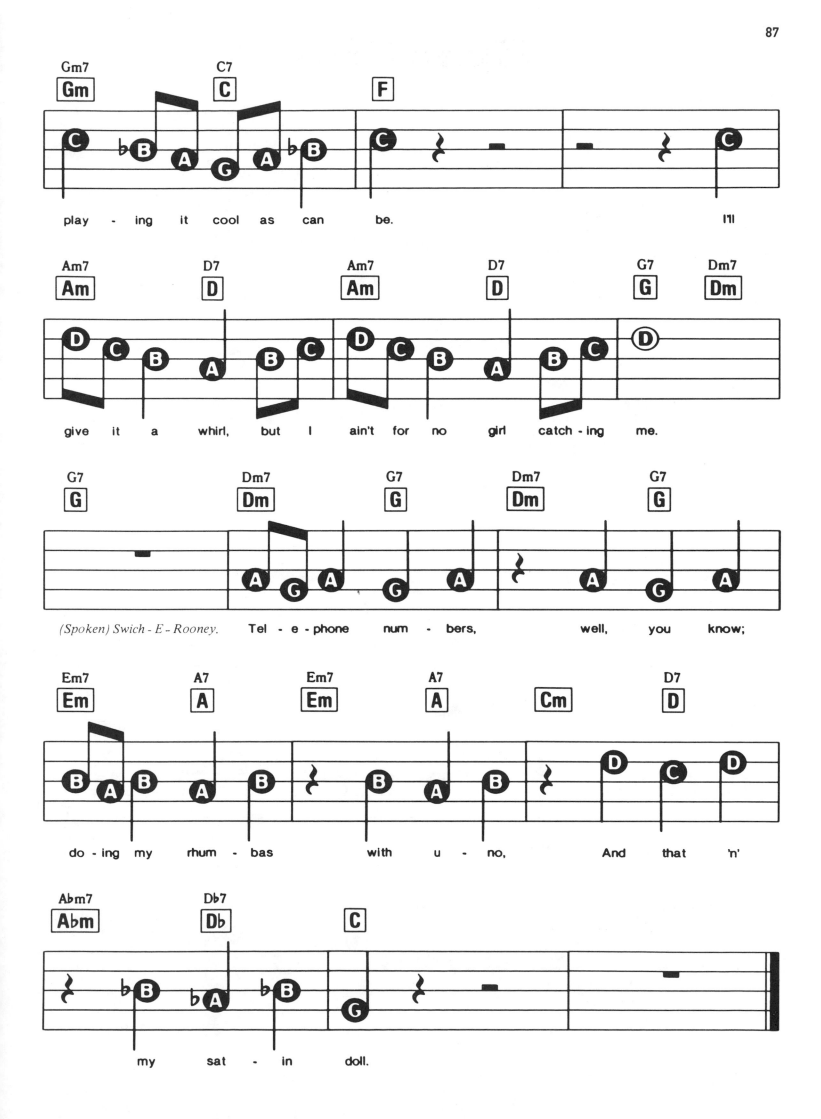

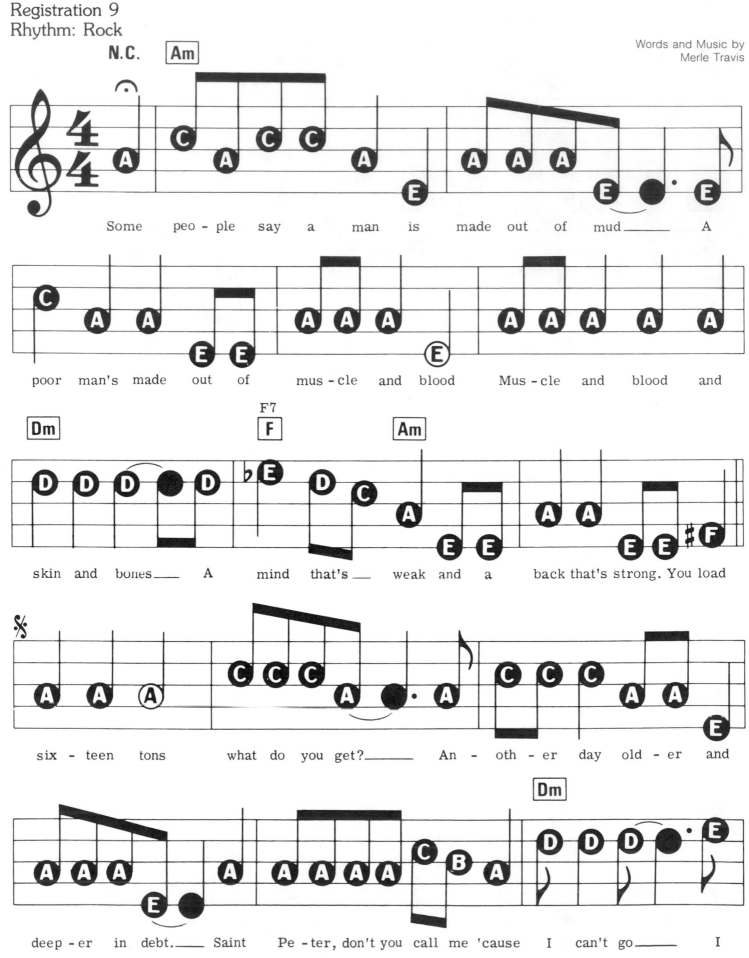

Sixteen Tons

Registration 9
Rhythm: Rock

Words and Music by
Merle Travis

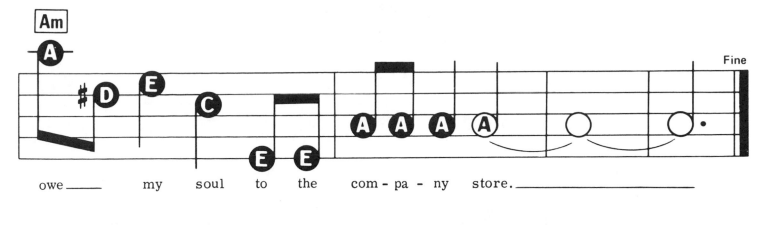

owe ___ my soul to the com - pa - ny store. _____

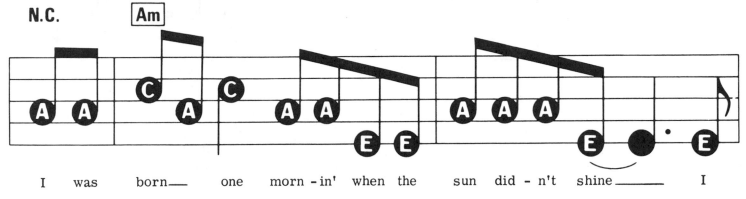

I was born ___ one morn -in' when the sun did - n't shine ___ I

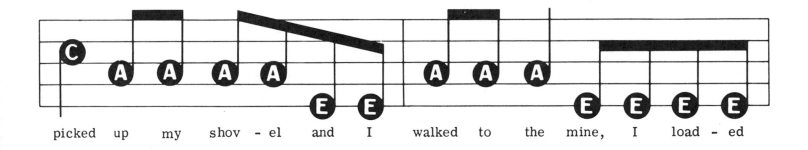

picked up my shov - el and I walked to the mine, I load - ed

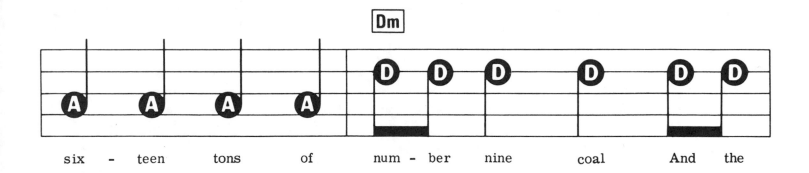

six - teen tons of num - ber nine coal And the

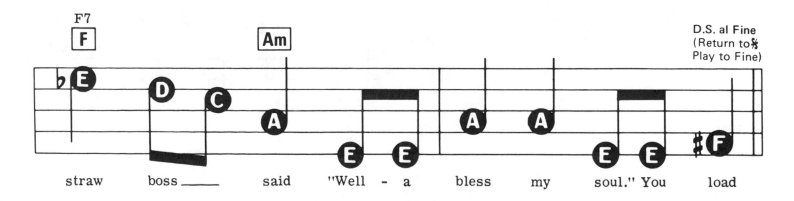

straw boss ___ said "Well - a bless my soul." You load

Smile
Theme from MODERN TIMES

Registration 9
Rhythm: Fox Trot or Ballad

Words by John Turner and Geoffrey Parsons
Music by Charles Chaplin

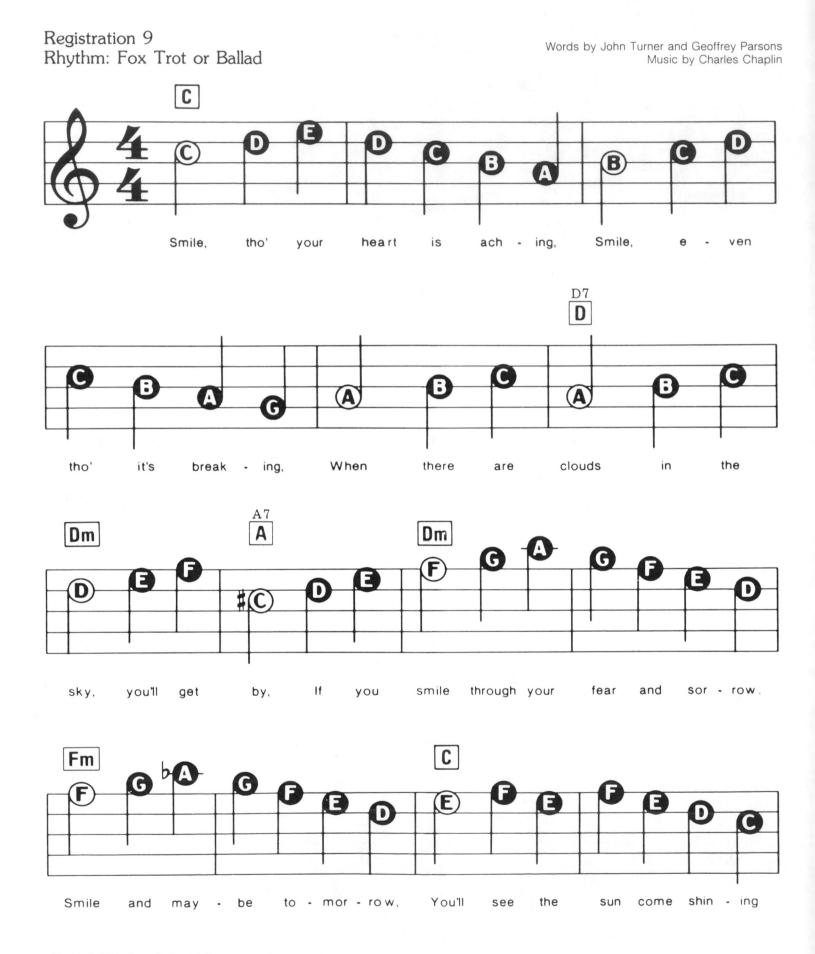

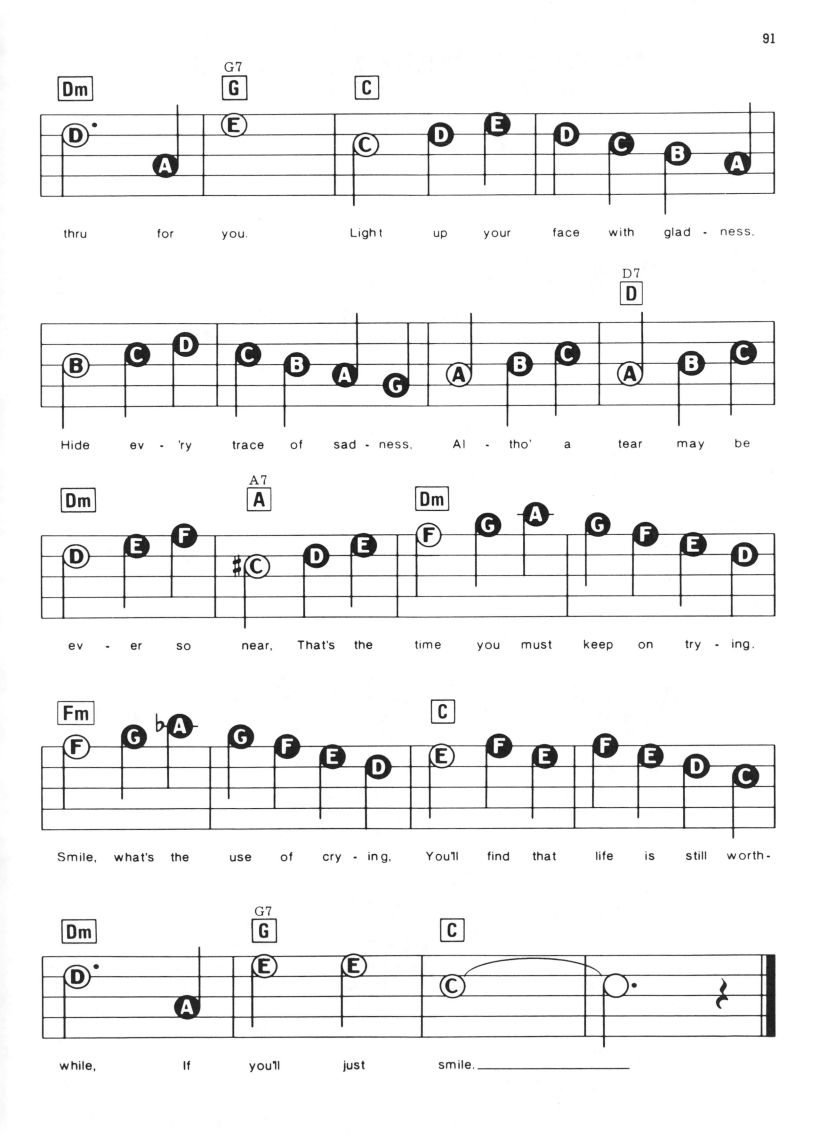

Summertime in Venice
from the Motion Picture SUMMERTIME

English Words by Carl Sigman
Italian Words by Pinchi
Music by Icini

Registration 9
Rhythm: Latin or Bossa Nova

N.C. · **C**

C B A G E· C E E C E G B A

I dream of the sum - mer - time ____ of Ven - ice and the

Dm7 / Dm · **G7 / G**

F· D F D C B A B B A B C

sum - mer - time. I see the ca - fes, ____ the sun - lit

Dm7 / Dm · **G7 / G** · **C** · **N.C.** · **E7 / E**

D B C D E E E E E B C D

days ____ with you, my love. The an - tique shop ____ where we'd stopped

Dm7 / Dm · **E7 / E** · **Am**

E D C· A C C C

____ for a sou - ve - nir. ____ The

93

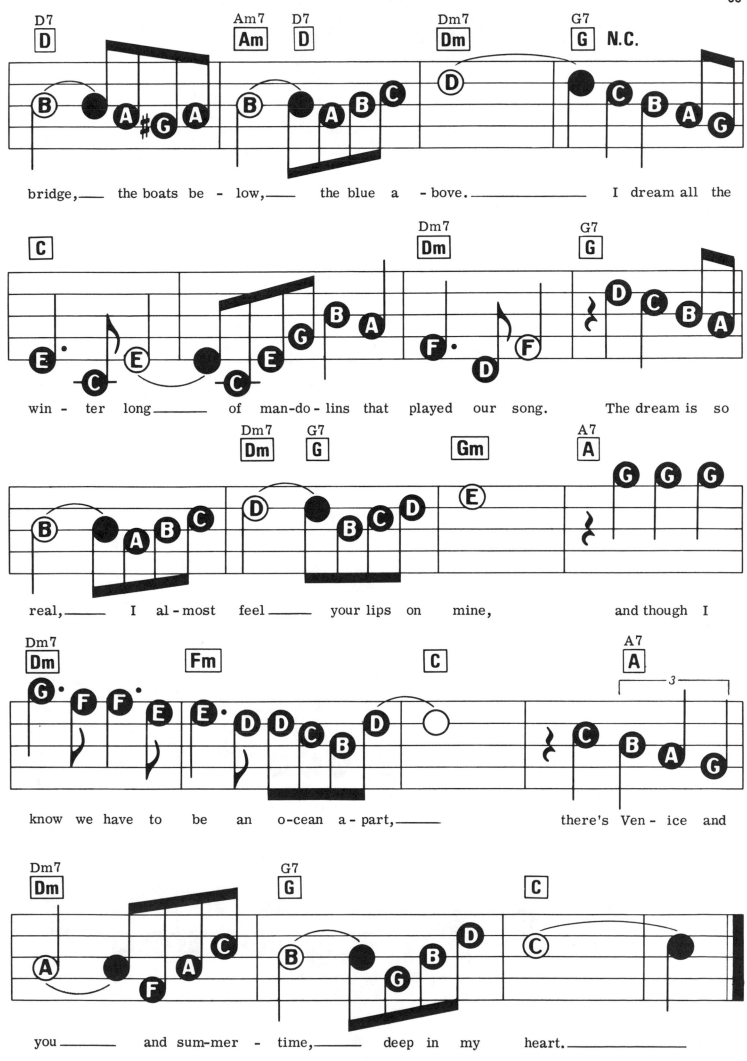

(Let Me Be Your)
Teddy Bear
from LOVING YOU

Words and Music by Kal Mann
and Bernie Lowe

Registration 1
Rhythm: Rock

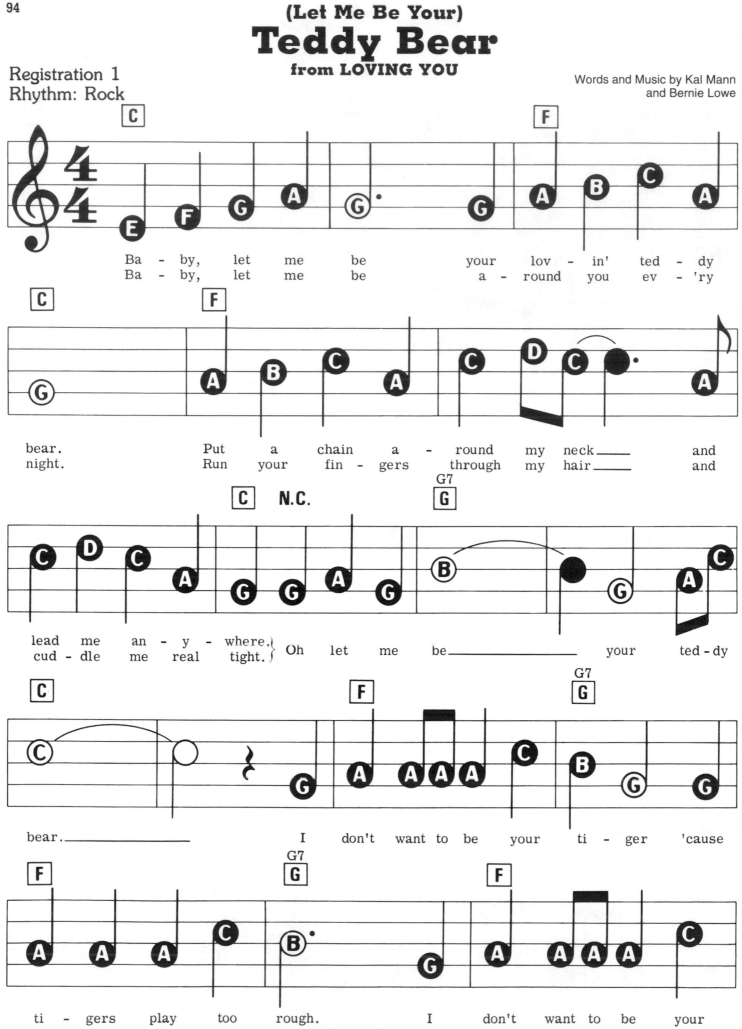

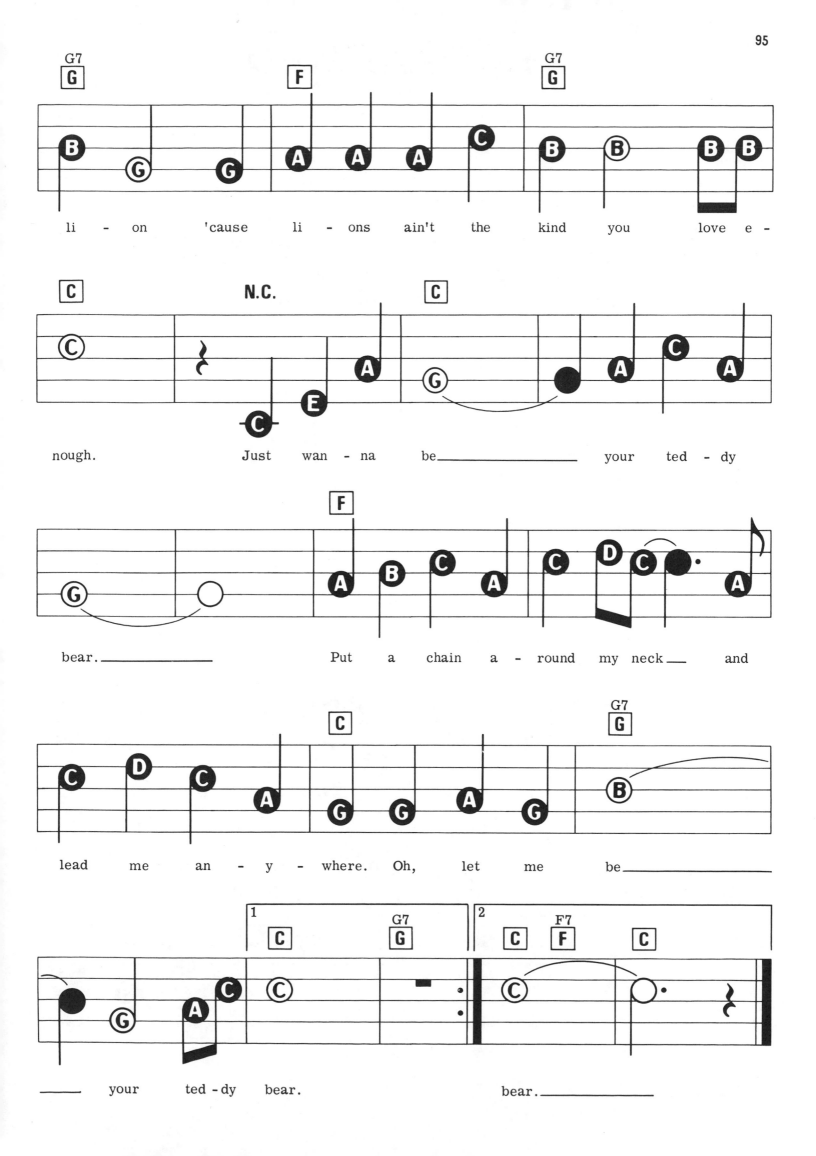

Tennessee Waltz

Registration: 4
Rhythm: Waltz

By Redd Stewart and Pee Wee King

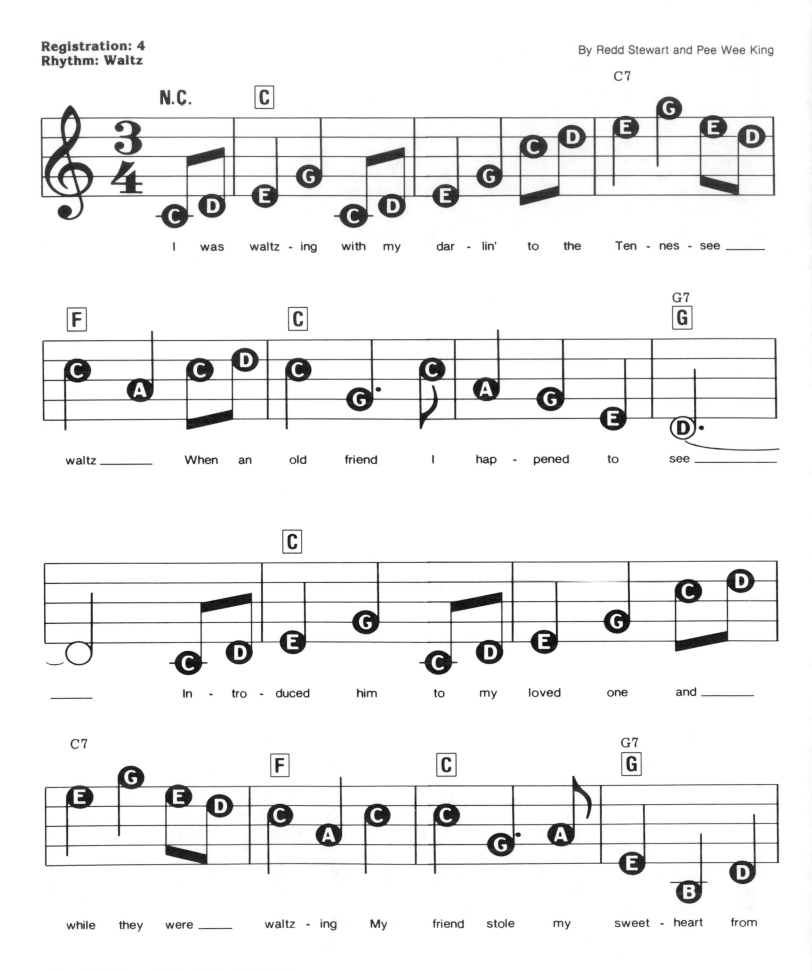

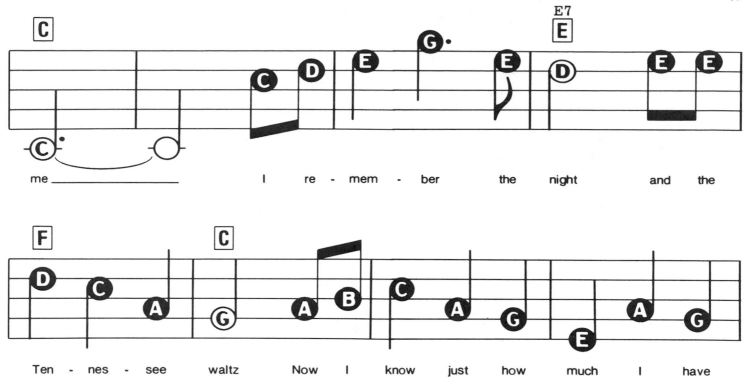

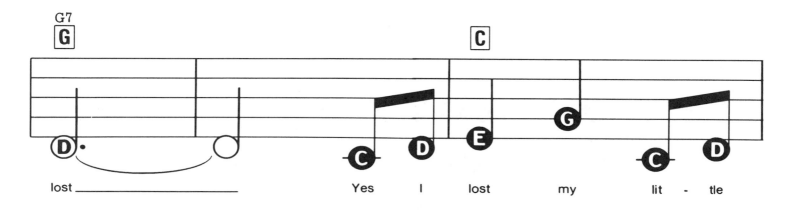

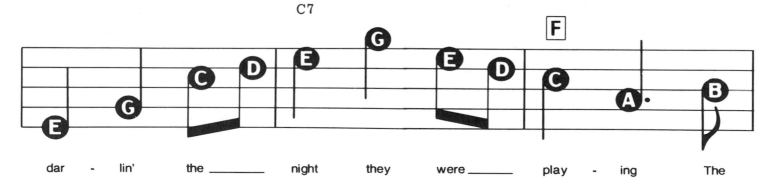

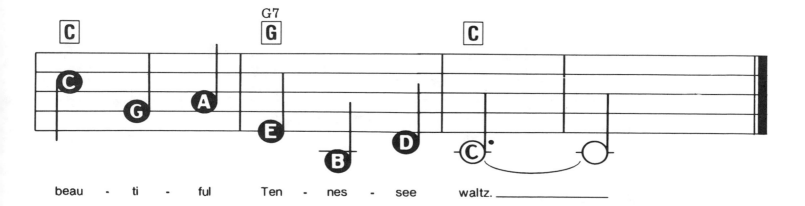

That'll Be the Day

Registration 8
Rhythm: Swing or Shuffle

Words and Music by Jerry Allison,
Norman Petty and Buddy Holly

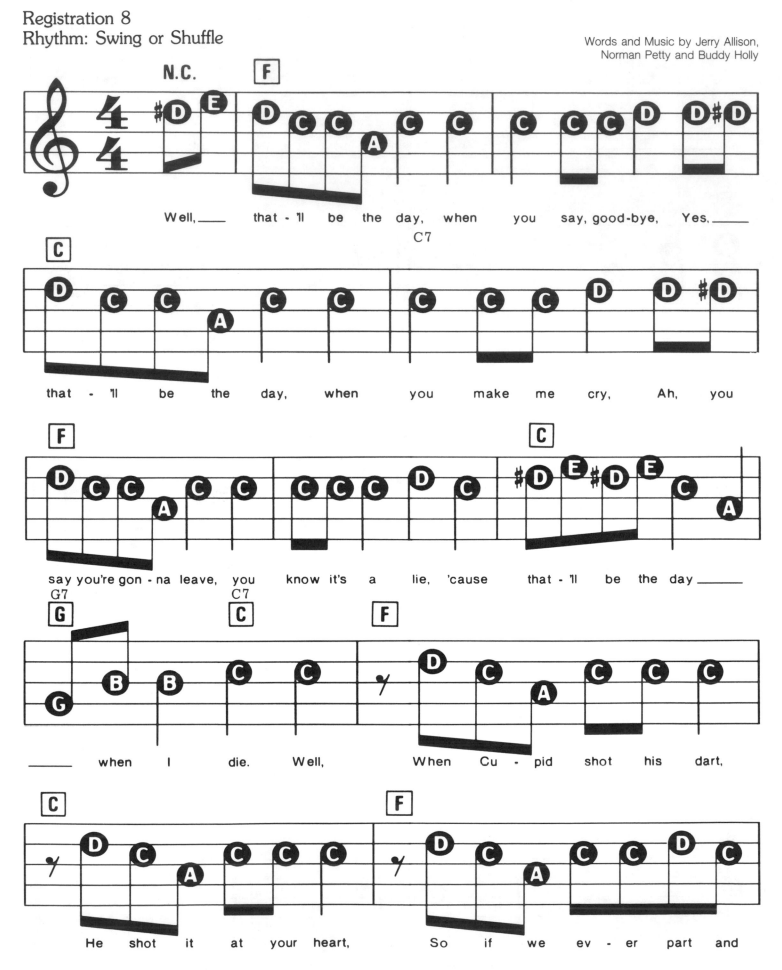

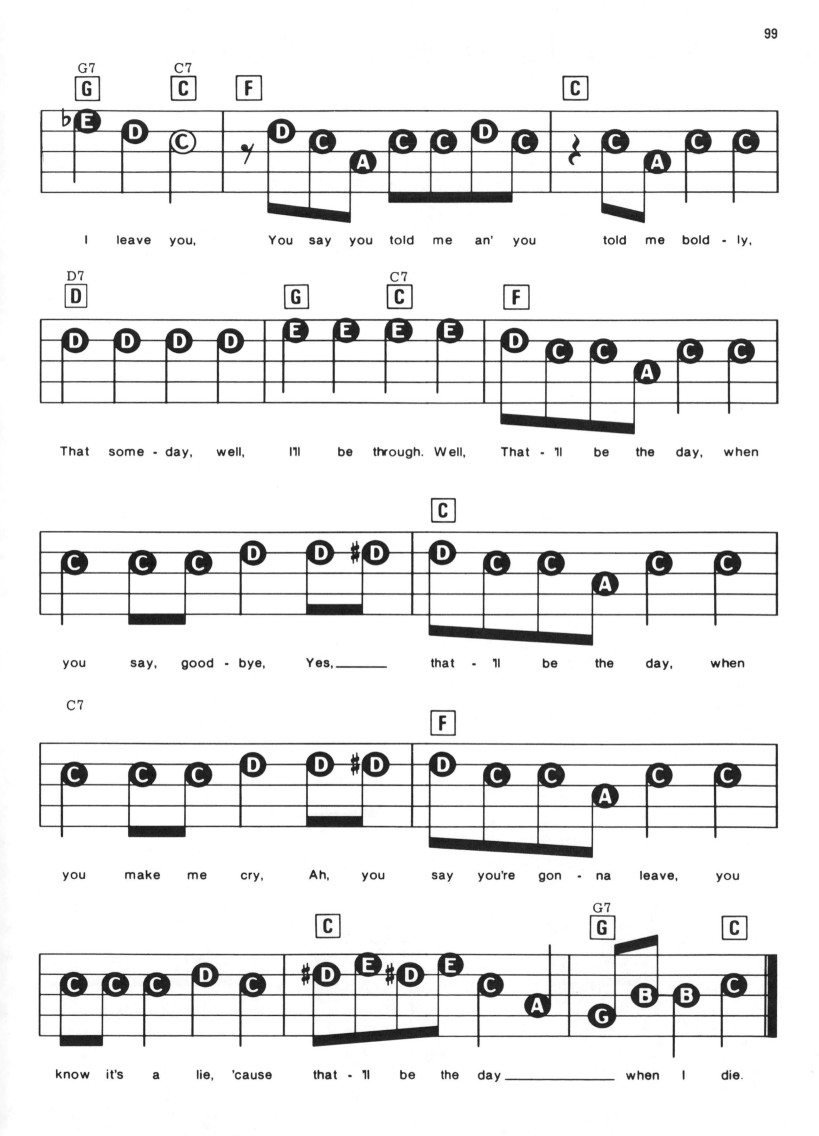

Three Coins in the Fountain
from THREE COINS IN THE FOUNTAIN

Registration 4
Rhythm: Ballad or Slow Rock

Words by Sammy Cahn
Music by Jule Styne

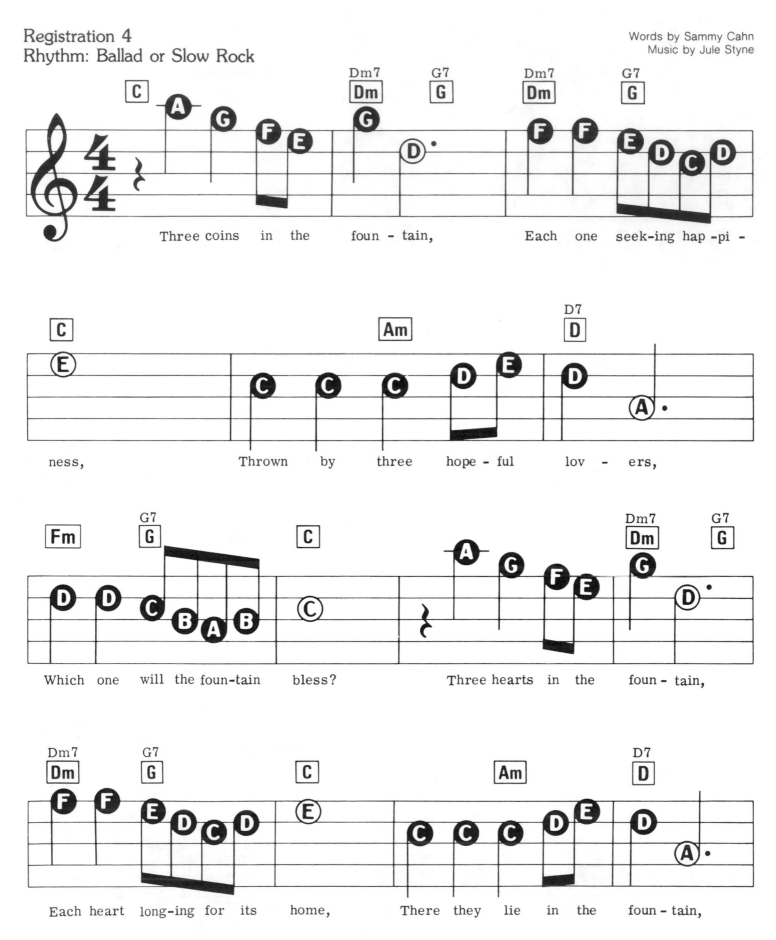

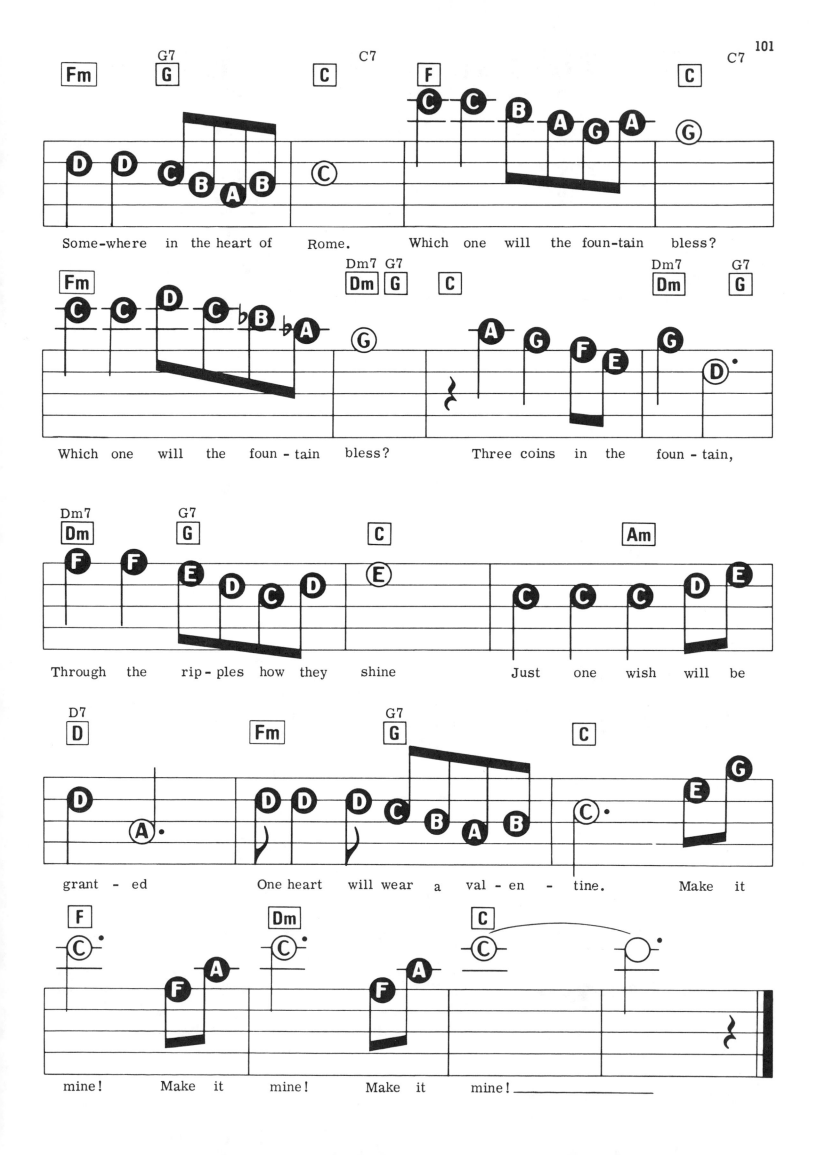

Till There Was You
from Meredith Willson's THE MUSIC MAN

Registration 2
Rhythm: Ballad

By Meredith Willson

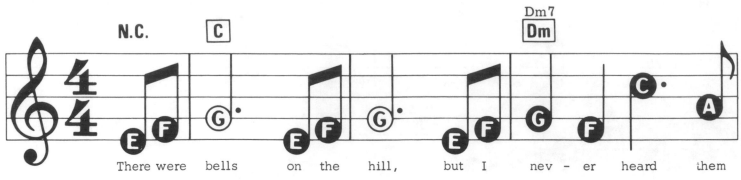

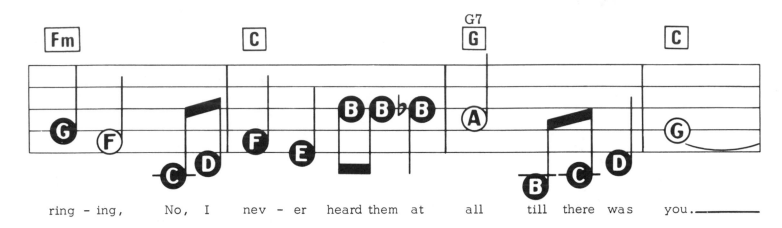

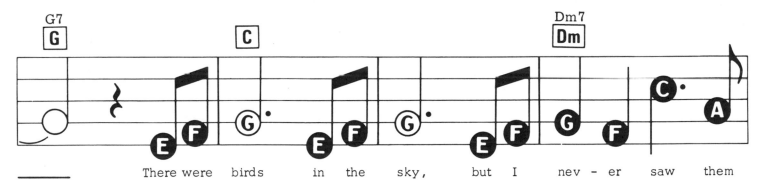

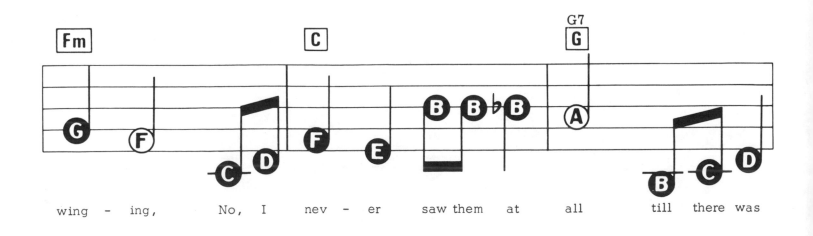

103

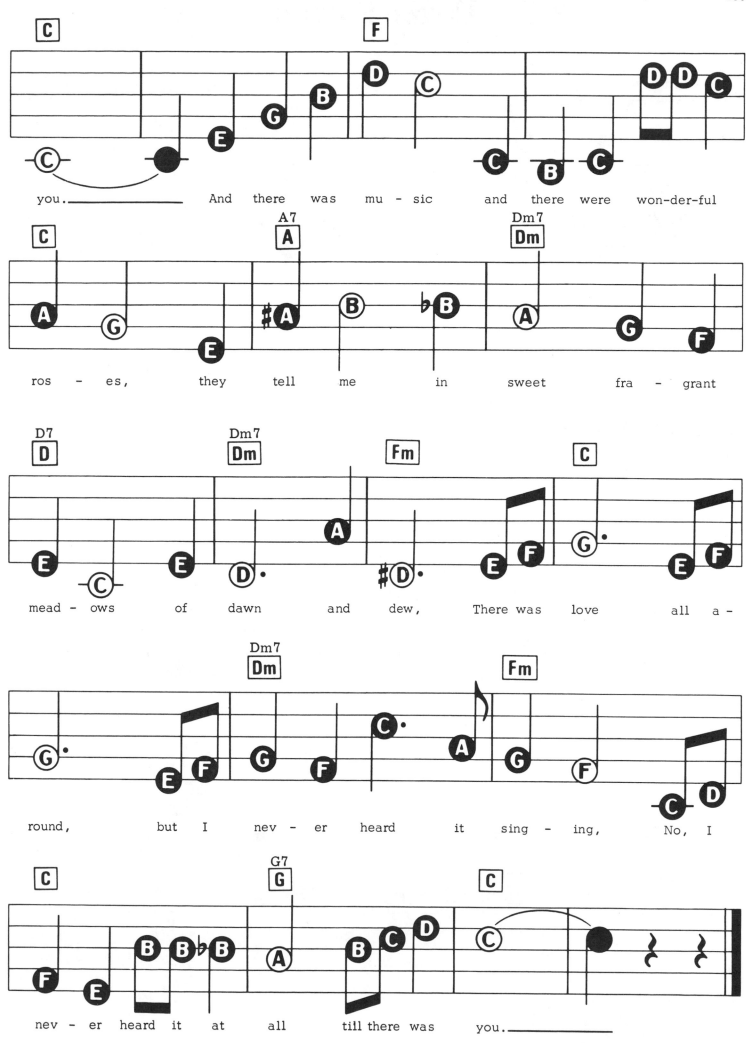

Tutti Frutti

Registration 4
Rhythm: Rock or 8 Beat

Words and Music by Richard Penniman
and D. La Bostrie

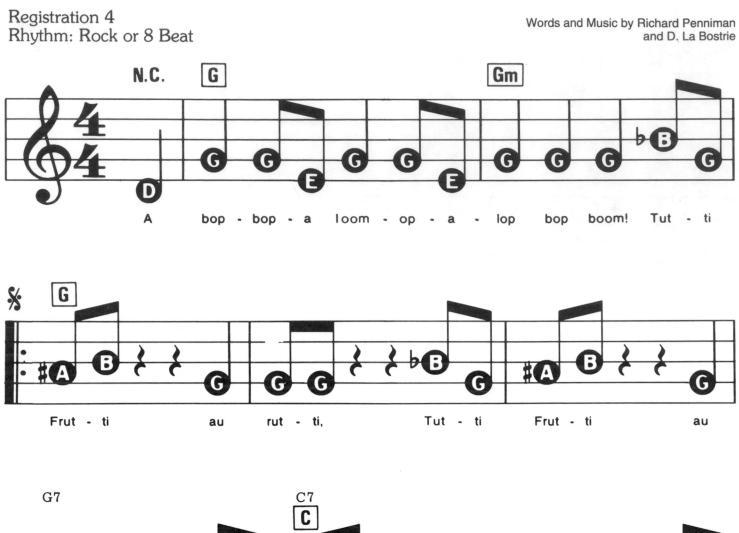

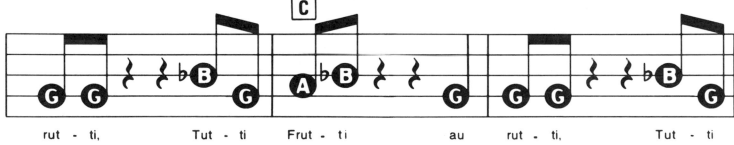

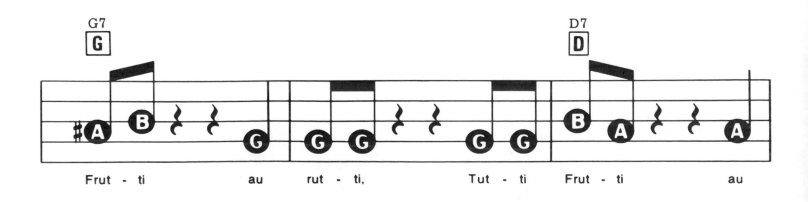

MCA music publishing

Unchained Melody
from the Motion Picture UNCHAINED

Registration 4
Rhythm: Ballad

Lyric by Hy Zaret
Music by Alex North

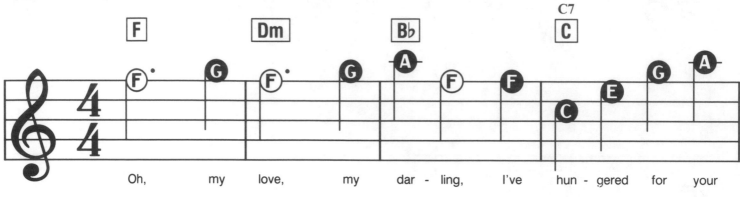

Oh, my love, my dar - ling, I've hun - gered for your

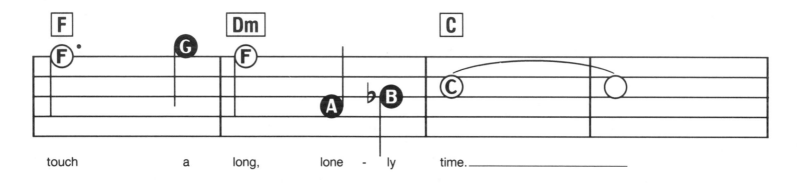

touch a long, lone - ly time._____

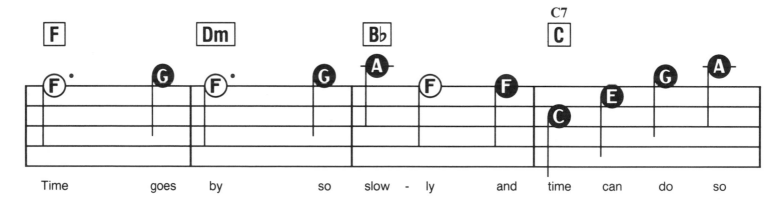

Time goes by so slow - ly and time can do so

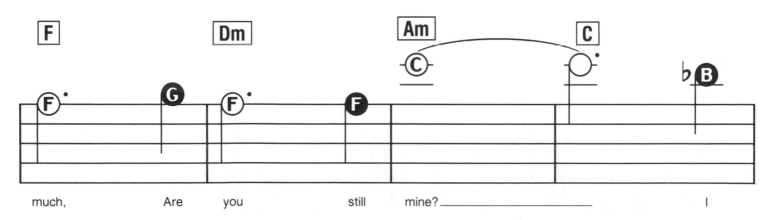

much, Are you still mine?_____ I

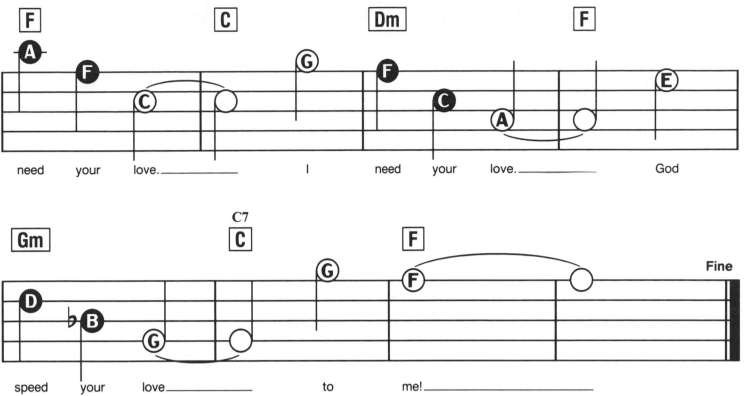

need your love.____ I need your love.____ God

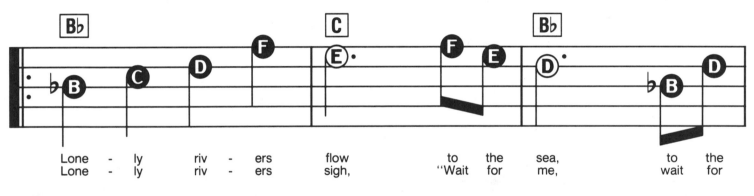

speed your love____ to me!____

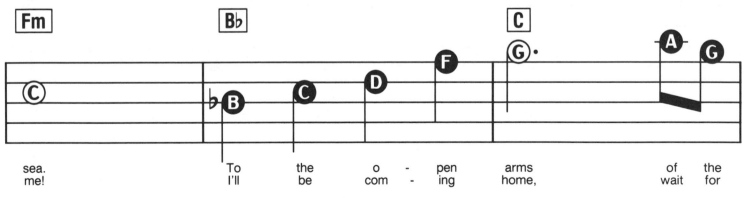

Lone - ly riv - ers flow to the sea, to the
Lone - ly riv - ers sigh, "Wait for me, wait for

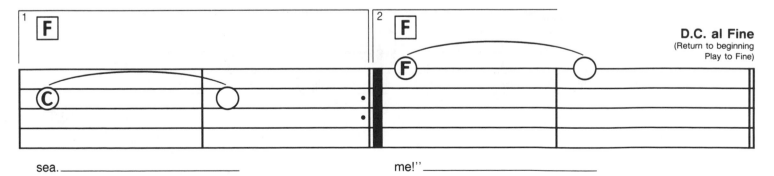

sea. To the o - pen arms of the
me! I'll be com - ing home, wait for

sea.____ me!"____

When Sunny Gets Blue

Registration 8
Rhythm: Ballad

Lyric by Jack Segal
Music by Marvin Fisher

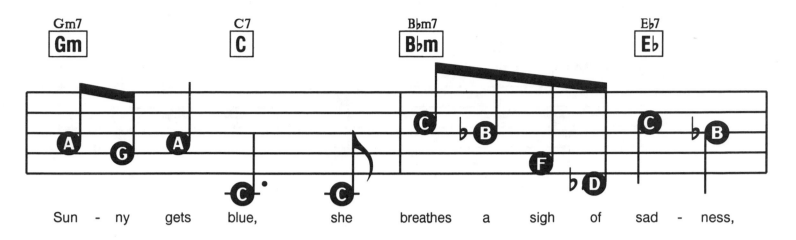

Sun - ny gets blue, she breathes a sigh of sad - ness,

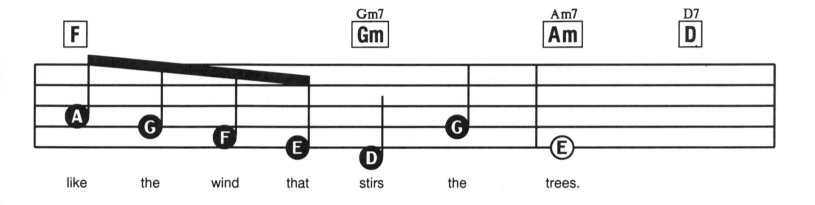

like the wind that stirs the trees.

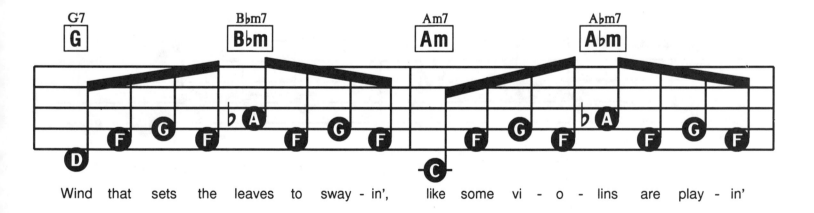

Wind that sets the leaves to sway - in', like some vi - o - lins are play - in'

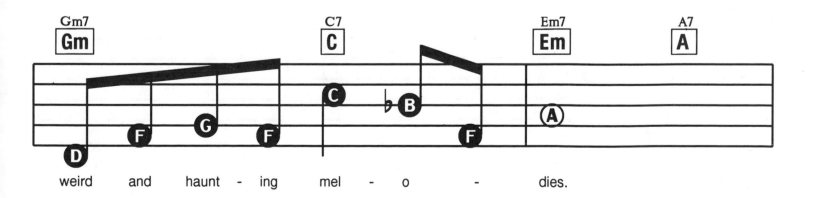

weird and haunt - ing mel - o - dies.

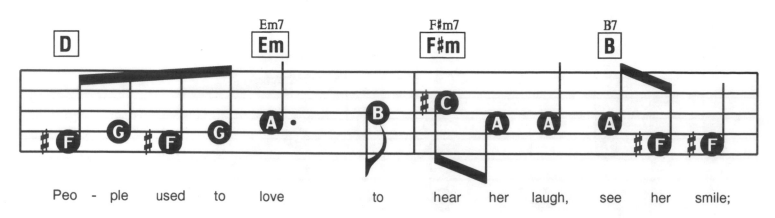

Peo - ple used to love to hear her laugh, see her smile;

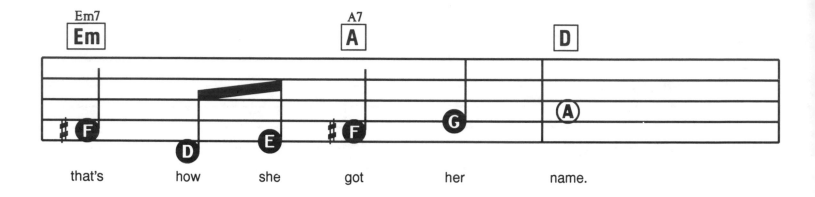

that's how she got her name.

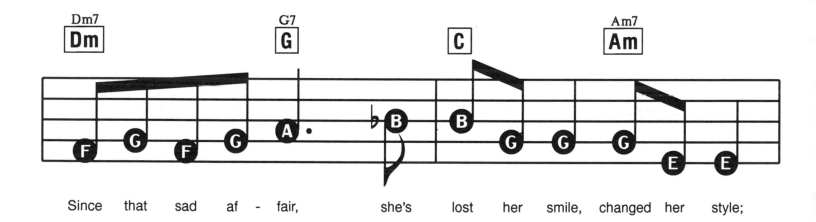

Since that sad af - fair, she's lost her smile, changed her style;

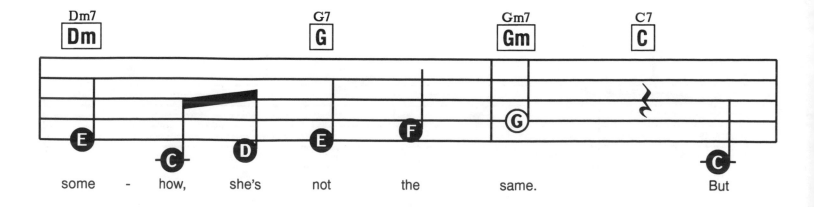

some - how, she's not the same. But

Witchcraft

Registration 9
Rhythm: Swing

Lyric by Carolyn Leigh
Music by Cy Coleman

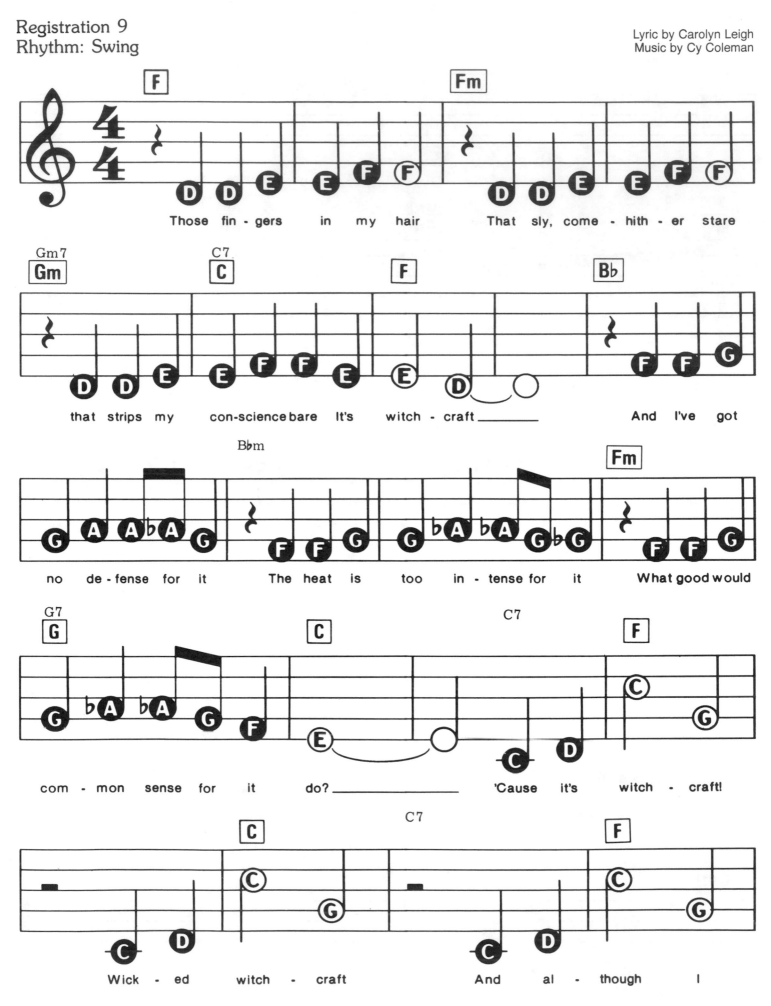

Your Cheatin' Heart

Registration 5
Rhythm: Country Western or Ballad

Words and Music by
Hank Williams

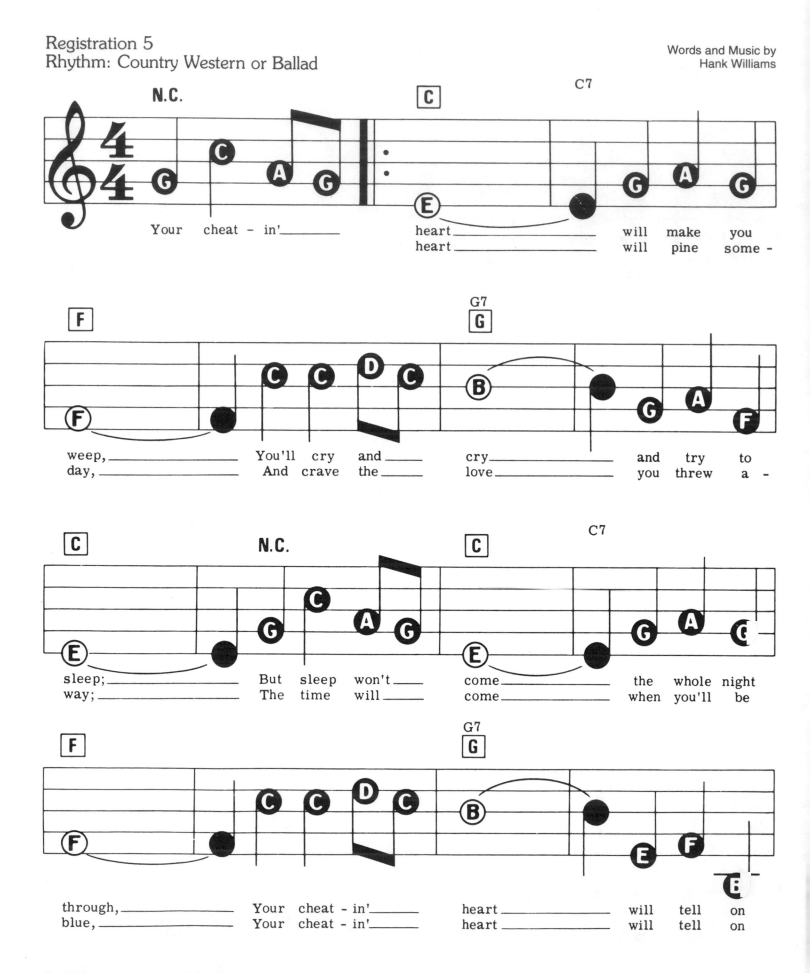

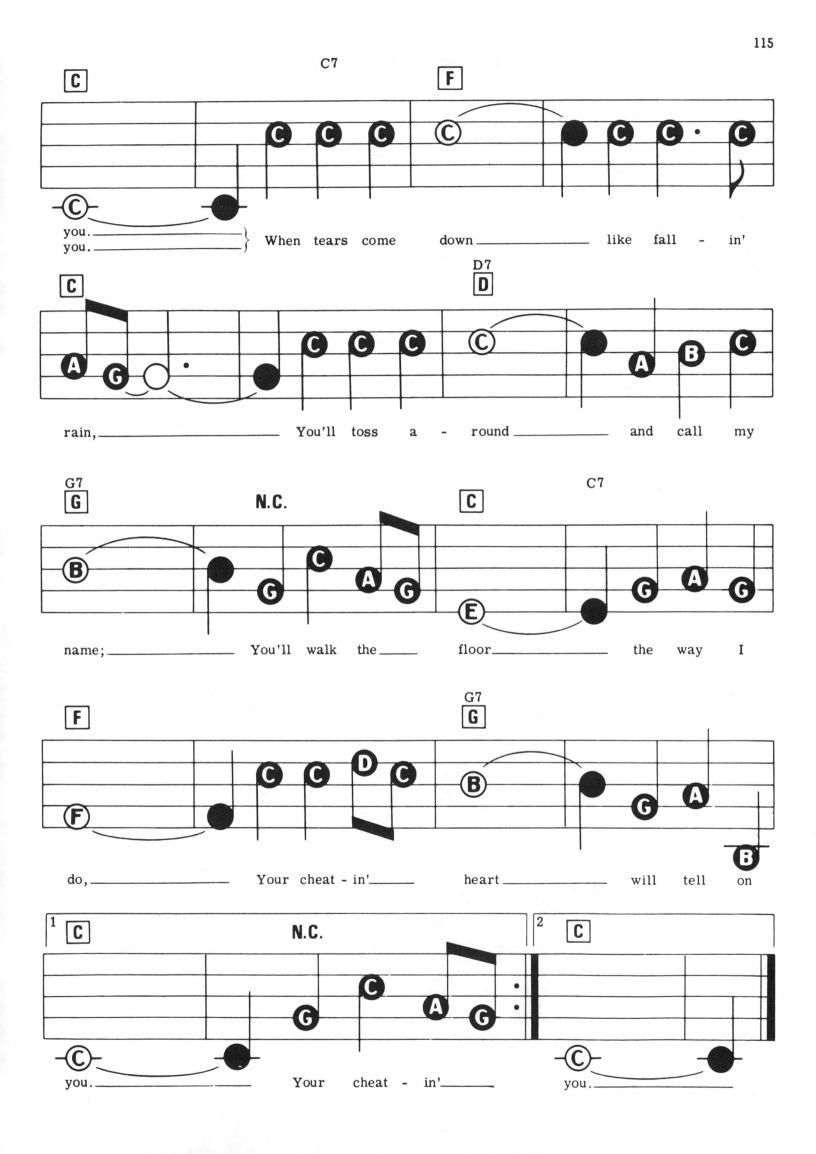

Too Much

Registration 4
Rhythm: Rock

Words and Music by Lee Rosenberg
and Bernie Weinman

Hon - ey I_____ love you too much.
You spend all my mon - ey too much.
Ev - 'ry time I kiss your sweet lips,

Need_____ your_____ lov - in' too much.
Have to share you, hon - ey, too much.
I can feel my heart go flip, flip.

Want_____ the_____ thrill of your touch.
When I want some lov - in', you're gone.
I'm_____ such a fool for your charms.

Gee, I can't_____ hold you too much.
Don't you know you're treat - in' me wrong.
Take me back, my ba - by, in your arms.

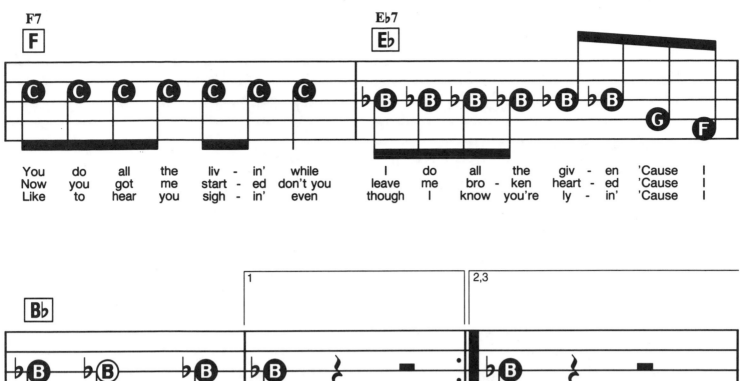

You do all the liv - in' while / I do all the giv - en 'Cause I
Now you got me start - ed don't you / leave me bro - ken heart - ed 'Cause I
Like to hear you sigh - in' even / though I know you're ly - in' 'Cause I

love you too much.
love you too
love you too

much.
much.

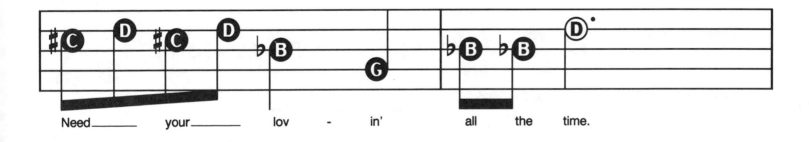

Need_____ your_____ lov - in' all the time.

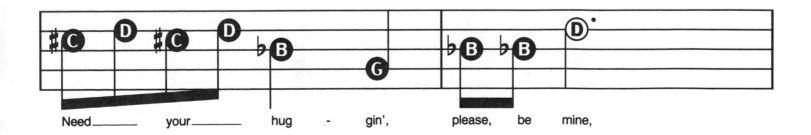

Need_____ your_____ hug - gin', please, be mine,

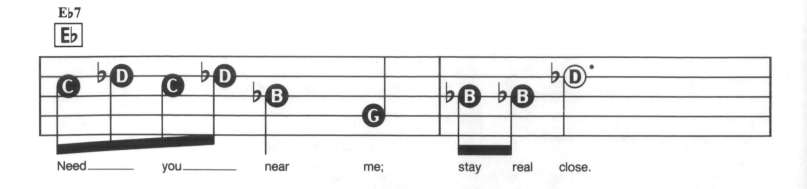

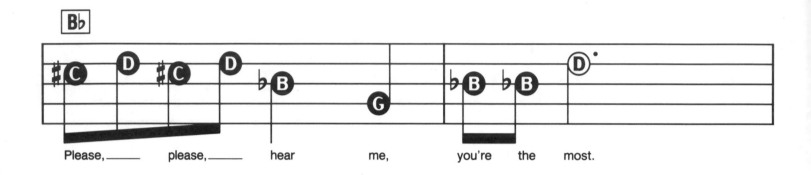

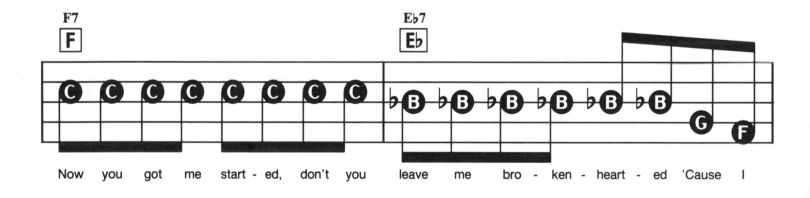

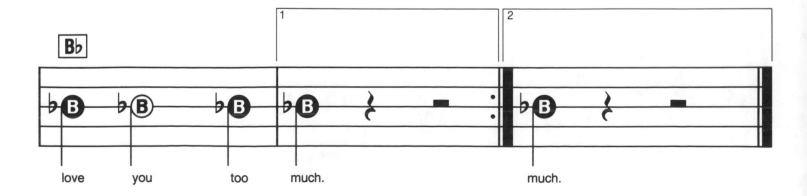

Registration Guide

- Match the Registration number on the song to the corresponding numbered category below. Select and activate an instrumental sound available on your instrument.

- Choose an automatic rhythm appropriate to the mood and style of the song. (Consult your Owner's Guide for proper operation of automatic rhythm features.)

- Adjust the tempo and volume controls to comfortable settings.

Registration

1	Flute, Pan Flute, Jazz Flute
2	Clarinet, Organ
3	Violin, Strings
4	Brass, Trumpet
5	Synth Ensemble, Accordion, Brass
6	Pipe Organ, Harpsichord
7	Jazz Organ, Vibraphone, Vibes, Electric Piano, Jazz Guitar
8	Piano, Electric Piano
9	Trumpet, Trombone, Clarinet, Saxophone, Oboe
10	Violin, Cello, Strings